High Fit – Low Fat

By   Lizzie Burt
and
Nelda Mercer, M.S., R.D.

ACKNOWLEDGMENTS

The authors wish to express their sincere appreciation to **Domino's Pizza, Inc.** and in particular to **Marge Monaghan** for their generosity, encouragement and help in publishing this book.

The authors also wish to recognize the direction and advice from the original and current members of the Cookbook Advisory Board:

LaVaughn Palma, M.A.	Judith Collins, R.N., B.S.N.
Katie Foran, R.N., M.S.	Carl E. Orringer, M.D.
Marge Monaghan	Lori Mosca, M.D., M.P.H.
Polly Minick	Melvyn Rubenfire, M.D.

We wish to thank **Barb Campaigne** for suggesting the title of the book.

We are particularly grateful to **Linda Wicklund, M.S., R.D.**, for her painstaking attention to detail in assisting with calculating the nutrient analyses. We also wish to acknowledge **Kathy Sadd, M.S., R.D.**, for her contribution to the training table.

We are grateful for the opportunity to work with Nashville's food photographer, **Mike Rutherford**, and food stylists, **Pat Coker** and **Doris Faucett.**

Our grateful thanks to **Mike Monahan** and **Frank Carollo** of **Monahan's Seafood Market** for sharing their wealth of knowledge about seafood in our recipes and cooking classes.

Special Thanks to **Katherine's Catering** for their loan of equipment supplies and their support of our cooking classes.

We are appreciative of those who attended our cooking classes for their encouragement and enthusiasm as we pursued the writing of this book.

We also wish to thank our friends and co-workers at **MedSport** and the **Domino's Pizza Fitness Center** for their cooperation in testing and evaluating our recipes.

How can we express our thanks and gratiude to our families for enduring many lonesome weekends—not to mention cheerfully eating the same dinner night after night in order to perfect these recipes.

Lastly, we wish to say a very special Thank You to **Mary Ann Fowlkes** for guiding us through to the finish line!

Published by Favorite Recipes® Press, P. O. Box 305142, Nashville, TN 37230
Copyright© 1989
Regents of The University of Michigan, P.O. Box 363, Ann Arbor, Michigan 48106

First Printing: 1989, 15,000 copies   Second Printing: 1990, 6,000 copies
Third Printing (Revised Edition): 1993   Fourth Printing: 1995
Fifth Printing: 1995, 17,500 copies

Library of Congress Number: 89-23360
ISBN: 0-87197-260-3

Printed in the United States of America

CONTENTS

Cover Photographs: Curried Pasta Salad with Shrimp and Asparagus and Light and Refreshing Blueberry Peach Crisp, pages 90 and 127

Domino's Pizza, Inc.
30 Frank Lloyd Wright Drive
P.O. Box 997
Ann Arbor, Michigan 48106-0997   Telephone 313-930-3030

After years of being a holdout to the fitness craze, a group of friends convinced me that it would be "fun" to work out and exercise. Years of a sedentary lifestyle, enjoying my needlework and cooking, had indeed made me apprehensive about this change in my routine. With the kids back in school and a weekend "eating spree" behind me, I decided it was time to give it a try.

At the Domino's fitness center, I met Lizzie Burt, a fitness instructor, who made the dreaded routine of exercising something fun and exciting. I also found that she was a gourmet cook and offered classes with Nelda Mercer, Registered Dietitian from the University of Michigan MedSport program, on healthy eating. Their recipes were not only healthy but really delicious. My favorite is "Pasta with Parsley Nut Sauce."

Both of these ladies inspired me into new eating habits which lowered my cholesterol and gave me insight into food and exercise. I encouraged them to put this book together, so their information could be shared with everyone. I hope as you read this book and try the recipes, you will benefit from their knowledge as I have.

Marjorie Monaghan

Marge Monaghan

University of Michigan
Medical Center

The focus of health care in the United States is moving away from intervention and toward prevention. Healthy People 2000 is an initiative by the Public Health Service which urges the health care community to direct its efforts toward disease prevention and health promotion. Healthy People 2000 includes 21 objectives concerning nutrition. Emphasis is also placed on physical activity, tobacco use, alcohol abuse, and food and drug safety. The U.S. Preventive Services Task Force, appointed by the Department of Health and Human Services to give health professionals recommendations regarding the above, emphasizes the role of behavior and nutrition counseling in disease prevention. Since five of the leading causes of death in the United States (heart disease, cancer, stroke, diabetes, and atherosclerosis) are related to nutrition, dietary modification may play a major role in improving the health status of Americans.

A major goal of Preventive Nutrition is to decrease the amount of fat, in particular, saturated fat, in the diet. The good news is that Americans have decreased their intake of fat over the past decade, and there has been a parallel decrease in the incidence of coronary heart disease. There may be more to the story than just fat. We now believe that diets rich in antioxidants and fiber may reduce one's risk for heart disease and cancer. It is important for individuals who begin to decrease the amount of fat in the diet to replace it with foods high in complex carbohydrates. Research in children has shown that although they are eating less fat, they often replace calories from fat with simple sugars. This may predispose them to dental caries and other health problems. The overall goal of Preventive Nutrition is total fitness.

Although "heart healthy" meals were once thought of as restrictive, they are now considered preferable by many individuals. This is in large part due to creative, tasteful ideas such as the recipes found in *High Fit - Low Fat*. At the University of Michigan Preventive Cardiology Program, we emphasize more fun and less fear with food. Lizzie Burt and Nelda Mercer, the authors of *High Fit - Low Fat*, have certainly made it easier for us to accomplish this. Food is essential to life and good nutrition is essential to health. We believe the key to making positive lifestyle changes is having good resources and involving family and friends. Enjoy!

Lori Mosca, M.D., M.P.H.
Clinical Assistant Professor of Internal Medicine
Assistant Professor of Epidemiology
Director, Preventive Cardiology, Research
   and Educational Programs
University of Michigan

Melvyn Rubenfire, M.D.
Professor of Internal Medicine, Division of Cardiology
Director, Preventative Cardiology
The University of Michigan

WELCOME...

...to **High Fit - Low Fat**. Our goal in writing this book is to help you implement healthful, delicious eating practices. The book started out as a collection of recipes that were developed and demonstrated to patients enrolled in the University of Michigan MedSport Cardiac Rehabilitation program. Since heart disease is the number one cause of death and disability in the United States, and since diet alone is a major contributing factor both in causing and preventing this disease, we felt that this collection of recipes and nutritional information would benefit the American public as a whole. These recipes were also incorporated into the *Domino's Pizza Fitness Center Recipe of the Month*, and have been enthusiastically received by the participants. In addition, the recipes and nutritional information have been provided to athletes in our sports medicine clinic.

Our recipes feature and incorporate the use of fresh, whole ingredients with minimal use of processed foods or refined sugars. Our goal is to introduce you to techniques and methods of low-fat cooking that are designed to decrease saturated fat and cholesterol and increase dietary fiber and complex carbohydrates. This method of food preparation may take you a little longer at first and require some planning, but the rewards of your health, your family's health and personal satisfaction are well worth the time investment.

We recognize that while changes in routine and lifestyle are hard to make, it helps to have an understanding of why such change is necessary. For many of us, change is a growing process that does not happen overnight. Those who succeed at change work at it in a positive way, usually over a long period of time. We suggest that you also take time to implement these changes and set goals that are comfortable for you.

Let's start out by first understanding a few basics.

Why Low Fat?

Fat has become the culprit of the American diet and currently accounts for about 40% of calories ingested. Although fat is an essential nutrient and necessary for health, too much fat has been linked to increased incidence of heart disease, obesity and certain cancers. Because of this, the American Heart Association, the American Cancer Society and the American Diabetes Association recommend that diets contain less than 30% of total calories from fat and that no more than one-third of these fat calories come from saturated fat.

What Is Saturated Fat?

Saturated fat is solid at room temperature and is found predominantly in animal sources such as fatty meats, whole milk dairy products and rich desserts. Saturated fat is also found in some vegetable sources such as the tropical oils: palm, palm kernel and coconut.

It has been learned that the saturated fat content of the typical American diet is the strongest contributor to raising blood cholesterol. The cholesterol in food also contributes, but to a much lesser extent. Sources of saturated fat are listed on Table 1, page 11.

What Are Unsaturated Fats?

Unsaturated fats can be classified as monounsaturated or polyunsaturated fats. Both are liquid at room temperature and are found predominantly in vegetable sources. Both monounsaturated and polyunsaturated fats lower cholesterol when substituted in the diet for saturated fats. Recent research indicates that while both types of fats lower total cholesterol, monounsaturated fats have not been shown to lower "protective" HDL cholesterol, as do polyunsaturated fats. In addition, high dietary consumption of polyunsaturated fats have been shown to increase cancer risk in certain animals.

Our dietary recommendations therefore advocate a more liberal use of monounsaturated, rather than polyunsaturated fats. Sources of monounsaturated and polyunsaturated fats are listed on Table 1, page 11. The recipes contained in this book are low in total fat and especially low in saturated fat. The use of monounsaturated fat sources such as olive oil or canola oil is promoted.

Note that although an attempt was made to have each recipe yield less than 30% total calories from fat, not all recipes meet this limitation. It is important to remember that it is the total daily intake of fat that should be reduced to less than 30% of calories. This allows you to combine a high-fat item with a low-fat item at the same meal and still maintain less than 30% of calories from fat for that meal. For example, the percent of total calories from fat for the Pear-Raspberry Tart is 41%. When you combine this selection with other lower fat foods in a meal such as the Meatless Lasagna at 23% and Potato Bread at 15%, the total percent of calories from fat for the entire meal is only 26%!

What About Carbohydrates?

You have just learned why it is important to reduce your fat intake to less than 30% of total calories. Of equal importance is increasing your carbohydrate intake to greater than 50% of total calories. That means that you should be consuming more than half of your calories as carbohydrate!

A good number of you will probably say: "How can this be?"

If you stop to think about it, our society evolved on a diet that was rich in whole grains, fruits and vegetables and only occasional servings of meat or fish. This diet was high in unrefined, complex carbohydrates and dietary fiber and low in saturated fats and cholesterol. It was not until the Industrial Revolution that Americans began to feast on refined sugar and fatty foods. These changes in our dietary habits along with a decrease in physical activity largely account for the increased incidence of obesity, heart disease and cancer.

As you try to retrain your thinking about the benefits of high carbohydrate diets, it will help you remember a very important fact—FAT, not carbohydrate, MAKES YOU FAT! If, however, you add fat to high carbohydrate foods, such as butter on your bread or sour cream on your potato, then that high carbohydrate food now becomes a high fat food and can contribute many more calories from fat rather than from carbohydrate.

Controlled scientific experiments have shown that calories from fat are uniquely fattening. One reason has to do with metabolic efficiency. The human body is very adept in storing dietary fat in our fat cells or adipose tissue. This is simply because when we eat fat, the fat is already in the chemical form, called triglyceride, which is the same form that is stored in the body. It, therefore, "costs" the body very little

energy in terms of metabolic activity to store fat. For example, if you ate 100 calories of pure fat, such as a tablespoon of butter or margarine, the body would need to burn 3% of these calories or 3 calories to turn the fat from butter to fat on your body! Therefore, 100 calories of dietary fat yields 97 calories of stored fat. On the other hand, to turn 100 calories of carbohydrate, for example one large potato, into fat would "cost" the body about 23% or 23 calories. In this case 100 calories of carbohydrate would only be worth 77 calories of stored fat.

The truth of the matter is that rarely does the body convert all dietary carbohydrates into fat. Most of the ingested carbohydrate is used for energy, especially if one participates in regular exercise, and the remainder is stored in the liver and muscles in the form of glycogen.

Another reason why it is better to eat carbohydrate is because a high carbohydrate diet actually seems to stimulate metabolism, which means that you burn more calories throughout the day, and at a higher rate. Part of the reason is because carbohydrate seems to stimulate the secretion of thyroid hormone, which speeds up metabolism and, also, stimulates the sympathetic nervous system causing an increase in heart rate and other metabolic processes. Some scientists feel that this alone may be responsible for 10 to 15% of our energy expenditure.

Of added benefit is that eating carbohydrates also increases the "thermic effect of food" or TEF. This means that eating carbohydrates slightly increases your body temperature as a result of increased energy expended for digestion. This is why you generally feel warmer after a meal than before you started eating.

Regardless of what your nutritional concerns are—to lose weight, to reduce risk of heart disease and cancer, to increase your athletic performance, or to just plain feel better—a high carbohydrate, low-fat diet makes sense!

Up to this point, our discussion has focused on complex carbohydrates which along with the benefits of metabolism, as mentioned above, also enrich the diet with protein, B-vitamins, minerals, and dietary fiber. Simple carbohydrates can be classified as two types: refined carbohydrates which include table sugar, honey, molasses, corn syrup, etc., and simple carbohydrates from fruits and milk. Simple carbohydrates are quickly absorbed into the blood stream. They are readily converted to glucose, which is used by the body for many metabolic processes. Simple carbohydrates from fruit and milk are nutritious because these foods also provide added vitamins, minerals, protein and dietary fiber.

Simple carbohydrates from refined sugar, on the other hand, are void of added nutrients and fiber and are, therefore, considered empty calories. Foods high in refined sugar also pose a significant risk to dental health and should be limited in the diet.

All simple carbohydrates and particularly refined sugar should be limited by persons with diabetes and those who have high triglyceride levels. Although refined sugars are used in some of the recipes, especially in the dessert section, most contain limited amounts. Those recipes that contribute more than 5 grams of sucrose per serving are identified as not recommended for persons with diabetes.

What Is Dietary Fiber?

Dietary fiber, often called roughage, is that portion of fruit, vegetables, whole grains, beans, nuts, and seeds that is not broken down by the body during digestion. Diets without an adequate amount of fiber have been linked to a number of diseases including heart disease, stroke, diabetes, obesity and cancer.

The typical American diet contains an average of 10 to 15 grams of dietary fiber per day. The National Cancer Institute recommends doubling that amount to between 20 and 30 grams per day. According to a currently published diet survey, only 10% of the American population consumes greater than 20 grams of fiber per day. It is best to increase fiber by eating a variety of whole grains, fresh fruits and vegetables, and dried beans and peas. The recipes in this book provide a good means to accomplish this.

How Much Sodium Is Safe?

Sodium is an essential mineral which is needed in small quantities by the body to regulate blood pressure and blood volume. Sodium is also needed to keep the nerves and muscles functioning properly.

Americans consume two to four times as much sodium as is needed. A high sodium diet may cause elevated blood pressure in sodium sensitive individuals and high blood pressure can increase one's risk of heart attack, stroke or kidney disease. The American Heart Association suggests that sodium in the diet not exceed 3000 milligrams per day.

The major source of sodium in the diet is from table salt (sodium chloride). Salt is 40% sodium and one teaspoon provides 2300 milligrams of sodium. Other foods that contribute to high sodium intakes are cured meats and commercially processed foods.

You will be pleased to find that most recipes in this cookbook use little or no added salt. Special attention has been given to the careful and creative balance of added herbs and spices to flavor and enhance food.

Should Women Be Concerned About Calcium?

Calcium is an important mineral. It gives bone its structure and is required for muscle contraction, blood clotting and nerve transmission. Calcium plays a major role in the prevention of osteoporosis which affects an estimated 20 million Americans. Postmenopausal white women are at greatest risk. The adult Recommended Dietary Allowance (RDA) for calcium is 800 milligrams per day. However, in 1987 the National Institute of Health panel on osteoporosis concluded that it was probably a good idea for the entire population to consume 1000 milligrams per day. Postmenopausal women may need up to 1500 milligrams per day. Along with estrogen therapy, regular weight bearing exercise such as walking, jogging and aerobics are important for maintaining healthy bones.

The best way to meet your calcium requirements is by eating a variety of foods that are rich in calcium such as non-fat dairy products, deep green leafy vegetables, broccoli, and dried beans and peas. Recipes included in this book incorporate a wide variety of calcium-rich ingredients.

Why Is Iron Important?

Iron is a trace mineral of vital importance for health. Iron is essential for hemoglobin formation, which in turn is responsible for carrying oxygen to the cells of our body. Insufficient iron intake over a period of time, especially in menstruating women, can result in iron deficiency anemia. Symptoms of anemia are fatigue, lethargy and irritability. The Recommended Dietary Allowance (RDA) for women of childbearing age is 18 milligrams per day. For men and postmenopausal women the iron requirement is 10 milligrams per day.

Endurance athletes can also develop a special type of anemia termed "sports anemia." Sports anemia has been documented in some athletes even when dietary iron intakes meet the RDA. Thus, the exact cause is more than likely due to a combination of reasons and can include any of the following:

- Increased destruction of red blood cells
- Increased iron loss from sweat and urine
- Reduced iron absorption
- Inadequate dietary iron intake due to restricted calorie intake such as in wrestlers who must make weight
- Inadequate dietary iron intake in vegetarian athletes who typically consume foods of reduced iron bioavailability.

Good sources of dietary iron are lean red meats, green leafy vegetables and dried beans and peas as well as iron-fortified cereals. Iron absorption can also be enhanced by eating these foods along with a good source of vitamin C, such as citrus fruits and juices, tomatoes, strawberries, melons, green peppers, potatoes and dark green vegetables. Recipes in this book contain a wide variety of these dietary iron food sources.

Sources of Fat and Effect on Blood Cholesterol Levels

Monounsaturated	Polyunsaturated	Saturated
Lowers cholesterol when substituted for saturated fat	High intakes lower HDL-cholesterol	Elevates LDL-Cholesterol

RECOMMENDATIONS

Best Choice	Acceptable Choice	Occasional Choice
Vegetable Oils Avocado Canola High Oleic Safflower High Oleic Sunflower Olive Peanut	**Vegetable Oils** Corn Safflower Sesame Soybean Soft Margarines or Mayonnaise Sunflower	**Animal Fats** Bacon Beef Fat Chicken Fat Fatty Meats Lamb Fat Lard Salt Pork
Fruit Avocado Olives		**Dairy Products** Butter Cheese Cream Ice Cream Whole Milk
Nuts Acorns Almonds Beechnuts Cashews Chestnuts Filberts or Hazelnuts Hickory Nuts Macadama Nuts Peanuts Pecans Pistachios	**Nuts** Brazil Nuts Butternuts Pine Nuts Walnuts **Seeds** Sesame Sunflower Pumpkin	**Nuts** Coconut **Tropical Oils or Shortenings** Coconut Palm Palm Kernel Cocoa Butter

Note: Foods containing fats are a mixture of monounsaturated, polyunsaturated and saturated fatty acids. Foods are listed in the columns according to the type of fatty acid that is most predominant in the food.

How to Use Nutritional Information

Several recent reports have issued dietary recommendations aimed to reduce risk of chronic disease. These reports include: The Surgeon General's Report on Nutrition and Health, the USDA's Dietary Guidelines for Americans, and the National Cholesterol Education Program's Adult Treatment Panel Report. The recommendations of these reports focus on decreasing dietary fat and cholesterol and increasing intake of foods high in complex carbohydrates and fiber. While these reports are well meaning and are designed to inform the public on the role of diet in health promotion and disease prevention, they fall short in providing the public with a means to accomplish and implement these recommendations.

High Fit-Low Fat is a collection of recipes designed to be low in fat and high in complex carbohydrates and dietary fiber. In addition, the nutritional information given per serving for each recipe will allow you to determine the adequacy of your daily diet. Here is how you can use the nutritional information from the recipes or menu selections to help you meet these dietary recommendations.

Recipe Nutritional Information Per Serving	Dietary Recommendations
Calories	Choose a dietary pattern in which energy (calorie) intake is consistent with calorie expenditure (see page 16 to estimate your calorie requirement)
Protein (grams) *4 calories per gram*	Intake should be 12 to 15% of calorie intake
Total Fat (grams) *9 calories per gram*	Intake should not exceed 30% of total calories
Saturated fat (grams)*	Intake should not exceed 10% of total calories
Cholesterol (milligrams)	Limit intake to less than 300 mg per day

*Please note that some recipes are not analysed for saturated fat because of insufficient nutrient data.

Carbohydrate (grams) *4 calories per gram*	Intake should be greater than 50% of total calories with an emphasis on complex carbohydrates
Dietary Fiber (grams)	Intake should be between 20 and 30 grams per day
Sodium (milligrams)	Limit intake to 2400 mg per day
Calcium (milligrams)	Intake for males should be 800 mg; for females, 800 to 1500 mg per day
Iron (milligrams)	Intake should be for males 10 mg; for females 18 mg per day

Exchanges

For those individuals who are on calculated diets using the exchange system (i.e. diabetic or weight watchers), the exchange values provide a means of incorporating these recipes into a prescribed meal pattern.

We recognize that while no guidelines can guarantee health or well being, good eating habits based on wise food selection can help you stay healthy and may even improve your health.

The following menu and nutrient charts are examples of how the recipes in this book can be used to provide a nutritionally complete diet for a reference male and female.

Reference Male:
Age: 35
Weight: 160
Body Frame size: medium
Activity: moderately active
(jogging 15 to 20 miles per week)

Reference Female:
Age: 25
Weight: 130
Body Frame size: medium
Activity: moderately active
(jogging 15 to 20 miles per week)

Menus

Breakfast	Male	Female
Fruity Bran Muffins	2	1
Low-Fat Vanilla Yogurt	1 cup	1 cup
Fresh Fruit in Season	1/4 melon	1/4 melon

Lunch

	Male	Female
Black Bean Soup	1 cup	0
Easy Veggie Baked Potatoes	1 serving	1 serving
Hearty Mixed Grain Bread	1 roll	1 roll
Blueberry Peach Crisp	1 serving	1 serving

Snack

	Male	Female
Super Thick Raspberry Shake	1 cup	1 cup
Marathon Morsels	2 cookies	0

Dinner

	Male	Female
Stuffed Breast of Chicken with Light Sherry Sauce	1 serving	1 serving
Zucchini Stir-Fry	1 serving	1 serving
Cranberry Conserve	2 tablespoons	1 tablespoon
Potato Bread with Oat Bran	1 roll	1 roll
Blackberry Sorbet	1 serving	1 serving

Snack

	Male	Female
Raisin Oat Bran Cookies	2 cookies	2 cookies
Skim Milk	1 cup	1 cup

Nutrients

	Calories	Pro g	%	Fat g	%	Sat Fat g	%	Carb g	%	Fiber g	Chol mg	Sod mg	Ca mg	Iron mg
Reference Male Requirement	2500	94	15	83	30	28	<10	344	>50	20-30	<300	<2400	800	10
Menu Totals	2495	104	17	47	17	12	4	432	69	60	90	2255	1883	22
% of Requirement	100	111		57		43		126		200	30	94	235	220
Reference Female Requirements	2000	75	15	66	30	22	<10	275	>50	20-30	<300	<2400	800-1500	18
Menu Totals	2010	88	18	35	16	11	5	347	69	43	89	1805	1697	17
% of Requirements	100	117		53		50		126		143	30	75	113-212	96

How To Determine Your Ideal Body Weight ①

=====

- Ideal body weight (male): 106 pounds for first 5 feet plus 6 pounds for each additional inch
- Ideal body weight (female): 100 pounds for first 5 feet plus 5 pounds for each additional inch
- -10% for small frame
- +10% for large frame

Frame size is derived by dividing height by wrist measurement

$$\frac{\text{Height in centimeters}}{\text{Wrist in centimeters}} = \text{Frame size in centimeters}$$

(Centimeters = inches x 2.545)

The chart below will give you your frame size.②

Female	Male	Frame Size
Greater than 11.0	Greater than 10.4	Small
10.1 to 11.0	9.6 to 10.4	Medium
Less than 10.1	Less than 9.6	Large

How Do You Determine The Number Of Calories To Maintain Your Ideal Body Weight ③

=====

1. Calculate the basal caloric requirements (the energy you expend at rest) by multiplying your personal weight goal or your ideal body weight by one of the following factors:

Age	Women	Men
Under 45	10	11
Over 45	9	10

2. Adjust caloric requirements for age by subtracting 10 calories for each year over 25 from your basal energy requirements.
3. Add calories for physical activity by multiplying the calories adjusted for age.

       sedentary (office work) 0.3

       moderately sedentary (occasional
          participation in an exercise program) 0.4

       moderately active (participation in
          a regular exercise program) 0.5

       extremely active (Olympic hopeful) 1.0

① ② ③ *Refer to notes on page 160 for additional information.*

TRAINING TABLE

Super Thick Raspberry Shake
page 33

Easy Veggie Baked Potatoes
page 30

Hearty Mixed Grain Bread
page 58

Light and Refreshing Blueberry-Peach Crisp
page 127

Marathon Morsels (2 cookies)
page 32

Per serving for complete menu: Calories, 1081, Protein, 34 g., Fat, 28 g. (total = 23% saturated = 6%), Carbohydrates, 183 g., Dietary fiber, 24 g., Cholesterol, 33 mg., Sodium, 817 mg., Calcium 731 mg., Iron, 9.5 mg.

"Eat To Compete"

Good nutrition is vital for optimal athletic performance. While it cannot replace a sound training program, what you eat, and when you eat it, can affect your athletic performance. According to the American Dietetic Association, the best nutritional advice for athletes is to consume a nutritionally balanced diet adequate in nutrients and calories to meet the energy demands of the specific sport whether it be walking, biking, jogging, running, tennis, swimming etc.

Photograph: Easy Veggie Baked Potatoes and Marathon Morsels, Super Thick Raspberry Shake pages 30, 32 and 33

THE TRAINING DIET

The following are a few guidelines which may help you to eat to compete.

Carbohydrates

Whether you're an athlete or not, carbohydrates are the ideal energy fuel for the body. The athlete's diet should consist of 60 to 70% carbohydrate. Complex carbohydrates should contribute most of the carbohydrate intake with simple sugars contributing only 10%. Studies indicate that complex carbohydrates promote significantly greater glycogen storage as compared to refined carbohydrates. Complex carbohydrates are also a good source of dietary fiber.

Protein

An optimal diet for an athlete consists of 12% to 18% protein. One common misconception among athletes is that a high protein diet maximizes muscle development and strength, thereby improving performance. It has been well established that protein plays only a minor role as an energy source during exercise. The major role of protein is for the maintenance and repair of body tissues. The recommended dietary allowances (RDA) for protein is 0.8 grams per kilogram adult body weight. Whether or not the RDA is appropriate for all athletes is not yet clear.

Most athletes consume at least twice the RDA for protein simply because of their increased food consumption. It is therefore not necessary, and in fact unwise, to consume protein supplements over and above the protein contained in a well balanced diet. Excessive use of amino acids and/or other supplements may cause nutrient imbalances and have potentially harmful effects. (see table Why Supplements? page 23)

Fat

Fat intake for the athlete should be kept to a minimum of 25% of total calories. Some athletes may wish to further lower their fat intake to 10 to 15% and to increase their complex carbohydrates accordingly.

PRE-COMPETITION MEALS

The goal of pre-competition meals is to provide adequate energy for full exertion without causing early fatigue or nausea.

Foods that are high in complex carbohydrates are your best choice (i.e. cereal, bread, bagels, crackers, potatoes, pasta, etc.). Foods high in fat or protein (i.e. meat, peanut butter, pastries, fried foods, ice cream, etc.) take longer to digest and may leave you feeling heavy and uncomfortable. Remember–you need the blood flowing to your muscles during exercises, not to your stomach–to digest a meal.

You may want to avoid sweet or sugary foods right before intense exercise. Foods such as dried fruit, juices, soft drinks, candy, etc., are high in simple sugar, which is quickly absorbed into the blood stream stimulating insulin secretion. Insulin is a hormone that carries sugar (blood glucose) into the muscles. Exercise, like insulin, helps carry blood sugar into the exercising muscles. The combined effect of increased insulin secretion plus exercise can cause your blood sugar to drop abnormally low (hypoglycemia) and may adversely affect performance. Symptoms of hypoglycemia include feeling light-headed, shaky, tired and uncoordinated.

PLANNING FOR THE BIG RACE

Most experts agree that meal timing is critical. Individual absorption rates, varying degrees of anxiety, and the duration of the event play a big role in determining *your* eating habits before competition. Recent studies reported at the American College of Sports Medicine meeting in May, 1989, recommend eating a fairly substantial high carbohydrate meal about three hours before a big race. However, it is very important to test **your** pre-race meal to be sure it works for **you**.

Short Races

Most of us doing short races early in the morning, such as 10 kilometers or less, will find that several tall glasses of water when we get up (essential for hydration anyway) will give us a feeling of fullness, dilute any raging gastric juices, and be sufficient to get us to the finish line. For further information about pre-competition eating and drinking for **Endurance Events**, see the chart on page 21.

Note: Use this as a guideline, then tailor it to your individual needs. Don't be discouraged if your eating arrangements are less than perfect the first time. Many of us are still experimenting after years of practice. Some people can eat a three-course meal an hour before a big race and do well, while others have to begin to taper their eating habits a day and a half before. The only constant is high carbohydrate, *low fiber* and low fat.

Why Low Fiber?

As previously mentioned, the optimal training diet consists of high complex carbohydrates, high fiber, and low fat. Only prior to competition should you limit your intake of high fiber foods. This is recommended in order to avoid unnecessary pit stops during the race.

TIME OF EVENT	CHOOSE RECOMMENDED FOOD
Before 10 a.m.	• Regular early dinner the night before—very low fat, low fiber and high carbohydrate, e.g. pasta with a light veggie sauce, rice pilaf or baked potato with non-fat plain yogurt • Small snack at bedtime (optional) • About 3 hours before—moderate breakfast, high carbohydrate, low fat and low fiber, such as a couple of bagels, some juice and fresh fruit if the event is longer than 2 hours.
Late a.m., early p.m.	2 to 3 hours before the event • Regular low-fiber, low-fat and high-carbohydrate breakfast such as a bowl of cream of barley or cream of wheat cereal with skim milk and nonfat yogurt, 1 or 2 slices of dry toast with apple butter and some fruit, such as a banana or an apple, and /or a glass of juice.
Mid afternoon	Before 9 a.m. • Regular low fat, low fiber and high carbohydrate breakfast • Moderate snack 2 to 3 hours before the event, such as a bowl of cream of wheat cereal made with water, with nonfat yogurt, dry toast or a baked potato with nonfat plain yogurt
Late p.m. early evening	• Regular low-fat, low-fiber and high-carbohydrate breakfast • Light lunch, such as a turkey pocket sandwich and a fruity blender shake • Low fiber, low-fat and high-carbohydrate snack 2 to 3 hours before the event, as suggested above

REMEMBER YOUR FLUID INTAKE

Adequate Fluid Intake is Essential to Safety During Exercise

The human body is more than 90% water. We don't have to lose much of this water before our chemistry just doesn't work properly. Under normal conditions, our fluid regulators keep the proportions more or less constant. Vigorous exercise may alter the balance so that athletes have to take steps to keep their fluid levels normal.

Fluid Replacement Prior to Endurance Exercise:

Several days before the event—increase your fluid intake. Water is the cheapest and best hydrator. Avoid alcoholic beverages and those containing caffeine as they promote fluid loss. You are sufficiently hydrated when your urine is clear and copious.

The morning of the event—drink 2 to 3 glasses of water when you get up, and 1 or 2 more just before the start. The water you drink just before the start will soon escape as sweat, it won't have a chance to get to your bladder. In a longer endurance event, such as the Ironman, you may want to take an electrolyte or carbohydrate supplement drink about 15 minutes before the start, but be sure you have tried it in training first.

Fluid Replacement During Exercise:

Drink at least every 10 to 15 minutes, particularly if the weather is hot and humid. Smaller amounts (1/2 to 3/4 cup) taken frequently absorb more efficiently. Do not wait until you are thirsty; the brain doesn't receive the message that your body is dehydrated until you have lost 1% of your body weight, and by the time you have lost 2% of your body weight your efficiency is decreased by 10 to 15%.

Electrolyte Replacement During Endurance Exercise:

Electrolyte replacement drinks vary in their composition, and there is much debate as to the best dilution and proportions. If you are planning to do an endurance event, it is important to practice drinking what will be available to you during the event. Find out from the race director what will be offered, and in what % dilution it will be made up. Life threatening sodium depletion problems, which are manifest as symptoms such as severe abdominal cramps, headache, chills, dizziness or increased urination, have been known to occur in some endurance athletes. Electrolyte replacement fluids should prevent or alleviate these symptoms; however in some cases they can exacerbate them. Only by practicing with several different types and dilutions will you know what works for you. The ideal dilution range is between 5-10% glucose or glucose polymers. If you do not replace your carbohydrate needs with electrolyte replacement fluids, try eating cookies and /or bananas. In events from 2 to 4 hours, you will need approximately 75 to 100 extra calories every half hour. For events of 4 to 6 hours duration, you require between 75 and 100 calories every 20 to 30 minutes.

Points to Remember:

1. Drink at least 4 to 6 ounces every 10 to 15 minutes during the event.
2. Drink, even if you are not thirsty.
3. Drink! Dehydration is life threatening.
4. Drink electrolyte replacements that you have tried in training if you are doing an event longer than 2 hours. Replace 75 to 100 calories in fluid or solid form every 20 to 30 minutes, depending on the duration of the event.

Fuel Replacement after the Event:

Carbohydrates, carbohydrates, carbohydrates! The most efficient restoration of glycogen takes place within 1 hour after the event. Good sources of carbohydrates are pasta, bananas, grapes, raisins and bagels.

SUPPLEMENTS–USE AND MISUSE

Athletes in training for competition are continually searching for ways to improve their performance. Often they attempt to use vitamin or mineral supplements or other substances with reported ergogenic effects in hopes that they may gain a winning edge over their opponents. While many of these products are generally harmless, others, when taken in inappropriate amounts, may actually hinder an athlete's performance by creating biochemical imbalances or symptoms of toxicity. The following chart lists supplements, their possible harmful effects, and recommended alternatives.

SUPPLEMENT	ALLEGED ROLE IN EXERCISE	POTENTIAL HARMFUL EFFECTS	RECOMMENDED ALTERNATIVES
Protein powders	Source of protein for growth and repair of muscle tissue	Excess may cause dehydration; extra protein calories may be stored as fat	Lean meats, fish, poultry, low-fat dairy products, egg whites
Amino Acids	Source of protein for growth and repair of muscle tissue	Long-term effects unknown. Unlike protein foods, they lack other important nutrients	Lean meats, fish, poultry, low-fat dairy products, egg whites
Caffeine	Central nervous system stimulant: increases heart rate, feelings of alertness, increased level of free fatty acids in the blood stream	May cause stomach upset, nervousness, diarrhea, dehydration irregular heart rhythms	
Amphetamines	Central nervous system stimulant, feelings of alertness, mood elevation	Dependence and addiction, irregular heart rhythms, increased blood pressure	
Bee pollen	Improved recovery, enhanced endurance	Unknown	
Wheat germ oil	Improved physical performance	Unknown	

SUPPLEMENT	ALLEGED ROLE IN EXERCISE	POTENTIAL HARMFUL EFFECTS	RECOMMENDED ALTERNATIVES
Carnitine	Enhances fatty acid oxidation, sparing glycogen	Muscle weakness	Lean meats, low-fat diary products
Sodium bicarbonate	Enhances short term anaerobic exercise by buffering lactic acid	Unknown	
Thiamin (B1)	Carbohydrate metabolism, normal nervous tissue	Relatively nontoxic	Pork, lean meats, enriched and whole grains
Riboflavin (B2)	Respiration, cellular energy release	Relatively nontoxic	Dairy products, enriched grains
Niacin	Fat synthesis, energy release, carbohydrate metabolism	Itchy skin, flushing, irregular heartbeat	Poultry, fish, peanut butter
Pyridoxine (B6)	Amino acid and protein metabolism, RBC formation	Liver and nerve damage	Herring, salmon, wheat germ, whole grains, lean meats
Folacin	RBC formation, regulation of tissue processes	Masks certain anemias	Wheat bran, whole grains, green leafy vegetables, legumes, orange juice
Vitamin B12	RBC development, nerve tissue maintenance	Liver damage	Fermented yeasts, fortified soy products, lean meats, low-fat dairy products, egg whites
Biotin	Fat and glycogen synthesis, amino acid metabolism	Depressed secretion of stomach HCL	Legumes

SUPPLEMENT	ALLEGED ROLE IN EXERCISE	POTENTIAL HARMFUL EFFECTS	RECOMMENDED ALTERNATIVES
Pantothenic acid	Energy and tissue metabolism	Diarrhea	Wheat bran, spinach, legumes, lean meats
Vitamin C	Maintenance of tissues, wound healing	Diarrhea, kidney stones, rebound scurvy	Citrus fruits, green leafy vegetables, tomatoes, potatoes, strawberries
Vitamin E	Maintains RBC integrity, normal muscle function	Fatigue, muscle weakness, lowered resistance to infection	Vegetable oils, wide variety of other foods
Calcium	Maintenance of skeletal muscle, normal muscle function	Urinary tract stones, nausea, diarrhea	Low-fat dairy products, green leafy vegetables, oysters, tofu, sardines
Iron	Hemoglobin formation, oxygen transportation	Constipation, poor copper and zinc absorption, nausea	Lean meats, oysters, tofu, green leafy vegetables, dates, kidney beans

ORIENTAL STYLE QUINOA SALAD

1 cup quinoa grains
1¹/₂ cups water
Pinch of salt (optional)
1 tablespoon pine nuts (or fresh water chestnuts)
2 tablespoons fresh coriander, finely chopped
1¹/₂ tablespoons fresh lemon juice
2 teaspoons sesame oil
1 tablespoon low-sodium soy sauce

1 large clove garlic, shoot removed and minced
1 teaspoon finely grated fresh ginger
³/₄ cup diced ripe tomato (one medium sized)
¹/₂ cup sliced fresh shitake mushrooms (if available, otherwise increase mushrooms)
1 cup mushrooms, thinly sliced

☐ Cook the quinoa by bringing it to a boil with the water and salt, reduce heat and simmer 10 to 12 minutes. You can tell when it's cooked because the little husks pop open to reveal a tiny translucent grain. Allow to cool a little.

☐ Roast pine nuts in your toaster oven or on top of the stove in a dry sauté pan, set aside. Combine the coriander, lemon juice, sesame oil, soy sauce, garlic, fresh ginger, tomato and mushrooms. When the quinoa is no longer hot, add this to the above ingredients and toss well, then sprinkle the pine nuts on top.

☐ Serve at room temperature as an accompaniment to fish or chicken, or as a main course accompanied by a hearty soup and crusty French bread.

☐ Makes 6 servings.

Variations: Try an Italian flair using fresh basil in place of the coriander, olive oil in place of the sesame oil, and omit the ginger. Use regular mushrooms, and boletus (if available). A French flair would substitute tarragon for the coriander, use olive oil instead of sesame oil, Dijon-style mustard instead of soy sauce and omit the ginger. Oyster mushrooms would be excellent (if available) in place of shitake. Indian style, substitute canola oil for sesame oil, 1 teaspoon curry powder for soy sauce, and almonds for pine nuts, and add ¹/₂ cup dark raisins. Omit the shitake mushrooms.

Per serving: Calories 127, Protein 6 g., Fat 2 g., 15% fat (2% saturated fat), Carbohydrates 22 g., Dietary fiber 6 g., Cholesterol 0 mg., Sodium 108 mg., Calcium 6 mg., Iron 1 mg.
Exchanges: bread 1; vegetable 1

HEARTY WHOLE GRAIN PIZZA CRUST

2¹/₂ cups hot water (105° – 115° F.)
1 tablespoon yeast
1 cup oat bran
3 cups white bread flour

3¹/₂ cups whole wheat bread flour
1 tablespoon canola oil
1 teaspoon salt

☐ Combine the water, yeast, oat bran and half the flour and wait until activity is visible (i.e. bubbles).

☐ Add the oil and salt; mix well. Gradually add enough of the remaining flour until the mixture cleans the sides of the bowl.

☐ Turn the dough out onto a lightly-floured surface and knead until smooth and elastic, adding small quantities of the reserved flour as necessary, until the dough is no longer sticky.

☐ Return the dough to a clean, lightly-oiled bowl, cover and place in a dark, warm, draft-free place to rise until doubled in bulk. This may take 1 to 2 hours, depending on heat and humidity.

☐ Preheat oven to 475° F. Turn the dough onto a lightly-floured surface, and divide into 2 equal parts. Set one aside, covered. Stretch the dough into a large rectangle or circle, depending upon the shape of your pan. This can be done with lightly oiled hands, or a lightly floured rolling pin. If the dough is resisting, allow it to rest a few minutes before proceeding. Arrange the dough on a lightly greased pizza pan, or cookie sheet. If using a stone, arrange the dough on a wooden paddle which has been lightly sprinkled with cornmeal. For a lighter thicker dough, brush with a little oil, cover, and allow to rise an additional ¹/₂ hour to 45 minutes. Cover the pizza dough with prepared sauces and toppings as desired, and follow cooking directions specific to the toppings.

☐ Makes 2 14-inch pizzas (10 slices per pizza).

Per 1 slice serving: Calories 150, Protein 5 g., Fat 1 g., 6% fat, (trace saturated fat),
  Carbohydrates 28 g., Dietary fiber 3 g., Cholesterol 0 mg., Sodium 108 mg.,
  Calcium 7 mg., Iron 0.8 mg.
Exchanges: bread 2

SPINACH PIZZA WITH SLICED TOMATO GARNISH

Although we are giving specific amounts and specific recipes here, pizzas are infinitely adaptable. Thus, your imagination should guide you to greater heights. Steer clear of the processed meats, high fat and sodium-laden ingredients, such as bacon, sausage and anchovies.

1 recipe sauce (see below)
2 pounds spinach, steamed, chopped and all liquid removed
1 teaspoon salt (optional)
1 to 2 tablespoons freshly ground green peppercorns (measure before grinding)
Freshly ground black pepper (optional)

1/2 teaspoon freshly grated nutmeg
8 ounces part skim milk mozzarella, grated (or crumbled feta)
3 medium-sized tomatoes, squeezed of excess juice before slicing

☐ Preheat oven to 475° F.

☐ Spread the prepared pizza dough (page 27) with sauce base (recipe follows).

☐ Combine spinach, salt, green peppercorns, black pepper and nutmeg and spread on top of pizza dough. Sprinkle with grated mozzarella cheese or crumbled feta. Garnish with tomatoes.

☐ Cook in the lower 1/3 of a preheated oven for 20 minutes or until the dough is well cooked and the cheese is melted and beginning to color. Tent with lightly oiled foil if cheese begins to brown before the dough is cooked.

☐ Makes two 14-inch pizzas (10 slices per pizza).

☐ NOTE: This is best on a whole grain crust that is fairly thick.

Sauce Base (Persillade)

3 large cloves of garlic, shoots removed and mashed
1 large shallot, finely chopped

1/2 teaspoon salt (optional)
1/2 cup parsley, finely chopped

☐ Combine all ingredients.

Per 1 slice serving: Calories 196, Protein 9 g., Fat 3 g., 14% fat (6% saturated fat), Carbohydrates 32 g., Dietary fiber 5 g., Cholesterol 6 mg., Sodium 358 mg., Calcium 132 mg., Iron 2.3 mg.
Exchanges: bread 2; fat 1

PIZZA TOPPINGS

Ideas for Other Topping Variations: (nutritional analysis not calculated) Use any variation and /or combination of the following.

Vegetables: Onions (sautéed slowly first on low heat in 1 teaspoon olive oil), mushrooms, green peppers, red peppers, pineapple (fresh), blanched broccoli or green beans, artichoke hearts packed in water (well drained).

Meat and Fish: Lean chicken or turkey (chopped), shrimp, crab, tofu.

Summer Salad or Gazpacho: On a basic dough which has been cooked with just the sauce and cheese, add your own toppings. These are some suggestions: chopped peppers, sliced mushrooms, bean sprouts, chopped tomato, shredded lettuce, chopped celery, chopped fresh herbs, chopped green onions. For serving this variation, offer the chopped garnishes in side dishes so diners can choose their preference.

TOMATO GARLIC SAUCE

4 cloves of garlic, finely chopped
1 teaspoon olive oil
2 pounds tomatoes, peeled, seeded and chopped*

1 tablespoon fresh (or frozen) basil chopped finely or herb of choice
1 tablespoon rich ruby port

☐ Sauté the garlic in the olive oil on low heat until transparent.

☐ Add the tomato, bring to a boil and simmer for 20 minutes.

☐ Add the fresh basil and port, return to a boil then remove from heat to cool before spreading on pizza dough.

☐ *May use 2 (14½-ounce) cans stewed tomatoes, drained, or 20 ounces of tomato purée.

☐ NOTE: This sauce freezes well.

☐ Makes about 3¾ cups.

Per 1 cup serving: Calories 248, Protein 9 g., Fat 7 g., 25% fat (3% saturated fat), Carbohydrates 45 g., Dietary fiber 7 g., Cholesterol 0 mg., Sodium 79 mg., Calcium 110 mg., Iron 5 mg.
Exchanges per 6 tablespoons: vegetable 1

EASY VEGGIE BAKED POTATOES

2 to 3 medium zucchini, cut julienne

6 large baking potatoes, scrubbed clean and pierced with a fork*

3 bunches green onions, white to pale green parts only, chopped finely (1 1/2 cups)

1 tablespoon olive oil

16 ounces fresh mushrooms, wiped clean and quartered

3 cups broccoli flowerettes, washed, blanched, cut into bite-sized pieces

1 red pepper, seeded, washed and cut julienne

2 (14 1/2-ounce) cans stewed tomatoes (no added salt)

2 large cloves of garlic, shoot removed and minced

1/4 cup fresh or frozen basil, finely chopped (if unavailable omit or substitute another fresh herb)

1/2 cup fresh parsley, thoroughly washed and finely chopped

4 ounces feta cheese, crumbled (skim or part skim if available)

4 ounces freshly grated part skim milk Parmesan cheese

Freshly ground pepper to taste

☐ Sprinkle zucchini with salt and allow to drain for 30 minutes. Omit this procedure if on a sodium-restricted diet.

☐ Bake the potatoes in a preheated 425° F. oven for 1 to 1 1/2 hours or until the skin begins to crisp and the flesh indents when pressed between the finger and thumb. May cook in batches in microwave and finish off in the regular oven to speed up the process.

☐ Sauté onions in olive oil until soft, add mushrooms and broccoli, cook for an additional 5 minutes. Add the red pepper and cook 2 to 3 minutes. Pat the zucchini dry and add it to the other vegetables, stirring occasionally.

☐ Meanwhile combine the tomatoes and garlic and purée. Add the basil and parsley and heat to boiling.

☐ Cut the potatoes in half, squeeze to soften and puff up their flesh then sprinkle each potato half with the cheeses. Add a little tomato sauce, pile on the sautéed vegetables and pour the remaining tomato sauce on top. Pass the pepper mill.

☐ Makes 6 servings. (photo page 17)

☐ NOTE: *Golden Yukon or white potatoes are best. Potatoes are best kept in a cool, dark, well ventilated cupboard. Reject any potatoes that are tinted green because they have developed a toxin which is inedible due to too much exposure to the light.

Per serving: Calories 461, Protein 20 g., Fat 12 g., 23% fat (6% saturated fat), Carbohydrates 74 g., Dietary fiber 9 g., Cholesterol 30 mg., Sodium 571 mg., Calcium 429 mg., Iron 6.8 mg.
Exchanges: lean meat 1/2; bread 3 1/2; vegetable 4; fat 2

BAKED POTATOES WITH FETA MUSTARD SAUCE

Vegetables In Season, Lightly Flavored With Crab Meat

1 bunch scallions, green and white parts separated and chopped
1 tablespoon olive oil
1 teaspoon minced fresh garlic (about 2 to 3 cloves)
6 ounces mushrooms, wiped clean and sliced thinly
3 cups broccoli, cut into bite-sized pieces
2 cups cauliflower, cut into bite-sized pieces
1 (10-ounce) package frozen peas

8 ounces fancy lump crab meat, sorted to remove any shell
1/4 cup dry Sherry
3 ounces feta cheese
1 tablespoon prepared mustard
6 large potatoes, scrubbed clean and baked until tender*
3 tablespoons pine nuts, lightly roasted
Fresh parsley, finely chopped for garnish

☐ Begin when potatoes are within 30 minutes of being fully cooked.

☐ Sauté the white part of the scallions in the olive oil until transparent (about 5 minutes), add the garlic, sauté 1 to 2 minutes more. Add the mushrooms and continue to sauté for an additional 5 minutes. Steam the broccoli and cauliflower in 3/4 cup hot water. Drain, reserving 1/2 cup of the cooking water.

☐ Add the frozen peas to mushroom mixture and cook until thawed. Add the crab meat and dry Sherry and cook until thoroughly heated. Add the green part of the scallions, the broccoli and cauliflower, stir well.

☐ Combine the feta, mustard and reserved cooking water in the bowl of a food processor or blender, process until smooth.

☐ To serve cut open the potatoes and pour about 2 tablespoons of the sauce in each potato, then pile high with the vegetable-crab meat mixture. Garnish with roasted pine nuts and parsley.

☐ Makes 6 servings.

☐ NOTE: *Golden Yukon or white potatoes are best.

Per serving: Calories 428, Protein 21 g., Fat 9 g., 19% fat (6% saturated fat), Carbohydrates 68 g., Dietary fiber 9 g., Cholesterol 33 mg., Sodium 687 mg., Calcium 169 mg., Iron 5.6 mg.
Exchanges: lean meat 1; bread 4; vegetable 1; fat 1

MARATHON MORSELS

These delicious cookies are high in fiber and flavor; kids of all ages love them!

1 cup graham flour or whole wheat
   pastry flour
1/2 cup oat bran
1 1/2 cups *old fashioned* oat meal
1 teaspoon cinnamon
3/4 cup golden raisins
1 cup dark raisins

1/2 cup packed brown sugar
1/4 cup canola oil
3 egg whites
2 teaspoons vanilla extract
1 teaspoon baking soda
1/2 cup pecans, coarsely chopped

☐ In a large mixing bowl, combine the first 4 ingredients plus half of the total raisins, set aside.

☐ In a food processor or blender, combine the brown sugar, oil and remaining raisins, purée. Add egg whites, vanilla and baking soda, purée just to combine.

☐ By hand, combine the liquid ingredients with the dry, mix well to incorporate. This makes a fairly stiff dough.

☐ Spoon onto lightly oiled cookie sheets, press a pecan piece into the middle of each cookie, and bake in a preheated 375° F. oven for 8 to 10 minutes, or until lightly golden.

☐ Makes 4 dozen cookies.

Variations: Substitute almonds or walnuts instead of pecans. Use chopped dried apricots, prunes or dates instead of raisins.

Per 1 cookie serving: Calories 65, Protein 1 g., Fat 2 g., 29% fat (3% saturated fat), Carbohydrates 11 g., Dietary fiber 1 g., Cholesterol 0 mg., Sodium 22 mg., Calcium 8 mg., Iron 0.5 mg.
Exchanges: bread 1/2; fat 1/2; fruit 1/2 (Not recommended for diabetics)

SUPER THICK RASPBERRY SHAKE

It's so thick you need a spoon!

**6 ounces raspberry-cranberry
frozen juice concentrate**
**12 ounces frozen raspberries
(no sugar added)**

**1 (12-ounce) can evaporated skim
milk**
**Fresh mint sprig and fresh
raspberries (optional garnish)**

☐ Combine the juice and raspberries in a blender and purée until they begin to break up. Add the evaporated skim milk and continue to blend until smooth. Pour into glasses and serve garnished with a sprig of fresh mint and a fresh raspberry if desired.

☐ Makes 4¹/₂ cups. (photo page 17)

BLENDER SHAKE VARIATIONS

Blueberry
12 ounces frozen (or fresh) blueberries
**6 ounces pure grape juice frozen
concentrate**

**1 (12-ounce) can evaporated skim
milk, or nonfat plain yogurt**

Cherry
12 ounces frozen (or fresh) cherries
**6 ounces pure cherry juice frozen
concentrate**

**1 (12-ounce) can evaporated skim
milk, or nonfat plain yogurt**

Strawberry
**12 ounces frozen (or fresh)
strawberries**
**6 ounces pure apple juice frozen
concentrate**

**1 (12-ounce) can evaporated skim
milk, or nonfat plain yogurt**

☐ Combine the blueberries and juice in a blender and purée until they begin to break up. Add the evaporated skim milk and continue to blend until smooth. Pour into glasses and serve garnished with a sprig of fresh mint and a few fresh berries if available.

☐ Makes 4¹/₂ cups.

Per 1 cup serving: Calories 185, Protein 7 g., Fat trace, Carbohydrates 39 g.,
  Dietary fiber 2 g., Cholesterol 3 mg., Sodium 99 mg., Calcium 254 mg., Iron 0.5 mg.
Exchanges: fruit 2; skim milk 1 (These calculations are an average of all shake variations.)

YOGURT CHEESE

Cream Consistencies

Yogurt is used widely in this book because of its nutrient content and versatility in substituting for cream consistencies. To obtain these different consistencies you need to drain some of the whey from the yogurt, and there is a handy funnel available at cooking supply stores for this purpose.

We have conducted a series of experiments using Dannon nonfat yogurt to give you some guidelines for achieving the different consistencies. The draining times vary widely. For example: If you want the consistency of sour cream, you need to remove approximately $1/2$ cup of whey from 2 cups of original yogurt. Use the following table as a guide:

Consistency	Drain	Approx Time Needed
Soft (such as sour cream)	$1/2$ cup whey per 2 cups yogurt	2 to 4 hours
Dry (such as cream cheese)	1 cup whey per 2 cups yogurt	6 to 7 hours or overnight

If you should drain too much whey from the yogurt, you can just fold it back in again. If you leave the yogurt more than a few hours after draining, you will notice more whey separates. Pour this whey off if you are going to use the yogurt as cheese or in a recipe that will ultimately be firm. When you are combining the yogurt with other ingredients that are to be puréed, do this by hand if you want to retain the firm consistency. For example, if you are making a savory yogurt cheese which you plan to spread, you will need a firm consistency, however if you are making a dip it's okay to incorporate the yogurt in the food processor.

Yogurt cheese has a long shelf life, at least as long as that of the original product, so we recommend that you have some drained in your refrigerator and ready for use at a moment's notice.

APPETIZERS & BEVERAGES

Blue Cheese Pinwheel Mold
page 37

Steamed Black Cod Steaks
page 81

Refreshing Wild Rice All Season's Salad
page 49

Crusty Whole Wheat Rolls
page 61

Baked Golden Delicious Apples in Blueberry Sauce
page 135

Per serving for complete menu: Calories, 619, Protein 32 g.,
Fat 11 g. (total = 16% saturated = 2%), Carbohydrates 101 g.,
Dietary fiber 18 g., Cholesterol 74 mg., Sodium 567 mg.,
Calcium 137 mg., Iron 4 mg.

Typically, this is the area where many excess calories may be consumed. However, the following recipes have been designed to be incredibly low in fat and high in flavor. You'll just love the easy blender shakes which can double up as dessert. Kids love them too! We encourage you to use the suggestions on presentation: remember before we eat with our taste buds we eat with our eyes!

Photograph: Blue Cheese Pinwheel Mold, Strawberry Blender Shake
pages 37 and 43

BLUE CHEESE PINWHEEL MOLD

This makes a particularly elegant presentation as an appetizer or hors d'oeuvre for holiday buffets both summer and winter.

The Base

1 cup lowest fat cottage cheese
2 ounces crumbled blue cheese
1 tablespoon green onion, finely minced
1 medium clove garlic, shoot removed and minced
1 tablespoon freshly squeezed lemon juice

1/2 teaspoon Worcestershire sauce
1 tablespoon fresh or frozen dill (1/4 teaspoon if using dry), finely chopped plus a few fresh sprigs for garnish
1/2 cup nonfat yogurt
2 teaspoons gelatin
1 to 2 tablespoons cold water

☐ In the bowl of your food processor or blender, combine the cottage cheese and blue cheese and purée until smooth. Add the onion, garlic, lemon juice and Worcestershire sauce, pulse to combine. Add the dill and yogurt and pulse again, just to combine. Sprinkle gelatin onto cold water; heat to dissolve. Add to cottage cheese mixture and pulse one or two times to combine.

☐ Pour into a 10-inch tart pan (one with a removable bottom lightly sprayed with vegetable cooking spray around the edges) and allow to set, covered, in refrigerator.

The Assembly

☐ Prepare a serving platter by lining it with mustard greens or similar greens. Unmold the base onto the serving platter.

☐ Place a single layer of shrimp to make a complete circle over the edge of the base, then the chopped olives followed by the diced tomato, diced cucumber and finally the remainder of the shrimp. Garnish the center with a tomato rose and some sprigs of fresh dill or parsley.

The Garnishes

8 ounces medium shrimp, cooked (frozen work well)
1/3 cup black olives, pits removed and chopped
Fresh dill or parsley to garnish
1/2 cucumber, seeded and diced

1 medium tomato, peeled and diced and drained of excess juice and seeds (make a tomato rose from the peel to garnish the center of the dish)

☐ Serve with crackers or thinly sliced French bread to accompany.

☐ Makes 10 servings or 20 hors d'oeuvres. (photo page 35)

Per serving: Calories 39, Protein 5g., Fat 1 g., 23% fat (15% saturated fat),
Carbohydrates 2 g., Dietary fiber trace, Cholesterol 25 mg., Sodium 97 mg.,
Calcium 39 mg., Iron 0.6 mg.
Exchanges: Lean meat 1/2; veg 1/2

SALMON PÂTÉ

8 ounces Yogurt Cheese
(see page 34)
3 ounces smoked salmon, chopped
finely
1 clove garlic, shoot removed,
minced

Dash of hot sauce
1 tablespoon fresh dill, lemon
thyme, or other herb (1/2 teaspoon
if using dry)
Freshly grated black pepper to taste

☐ Combine all ingredients, mix well. Press into a ramekin and garnish with the herb of your choice.

☐ Makes 1 1/2 cups.

Per 2 tablespoon serving: Calories 17, Protein 2 g., Fat trace, Carbohydrates 2 g.,
Dietary fiber trace, Cholesterol 1 mg., Sodium 46 mg., Calcium 43 mg., Iron trace.
Exchanges: skim milk 1/2 (per 1/4 cup serving)

Herb Cheese Variation: Omit the smoked salmon and add:

1/4 cup cottage cheese
2 tablespoons finely grated part
skim milk Parmesan cheese
1 tablespoon fresh parsley, finely
chopped

1 tablespoon snipped fresh chives
1 teaspoon miso, or 1 tablespoon
soy sauce
1 teaspoon lemon juice
1/2 teaspoon salt (optional)

☐ In the processor or blender, purée the cottage cheese, Parmesan cheese, herbs, miso or soy sauce and lemon juice. Transfer to a mixing bowl and fold in yogurt cheese. Stir in salt if desired.

☐ Makes 1 1/2 cups.

☐ NOTE: This is great served with thin slices of potato bread, stuffed into cherry tomatoes as an appetizer or accompanied by tomato slices, sprouts and lettuce in a pita pocket for a light lunch.

Per 2 tablespoon serving: Calories 45, Protein 5 g., Fat 1 g., 20% fat (7% saturated fat),
Carbohydrates 5 g., Dietary fiber trace, Cholesterol 2 mg., Sodium 253 mg.,
Calcium 137 mg., Iron .2 mg.
Exchanges: skim milk 1/2

GUACAMOLE

2 ripe avocados, mashed with a
  fork or potato masher
2 tablespoons freshly squeezed lime
  juice
1 tomatillo (optional), finely
  chopped
1 ripe tomato, finely chopped

4 scallions, finely chopped
1/4 teaspoon salt, or to taste
Freshly ground pepper
1 tablespoon fresh coriander,
  coarsely chopped
Dash hot sauce to taste
1 cup nonfat plain yogurt, optional*

☐ Combine all ingredients, taste and adjust seasonings. To avoid discoloration, reserve 1 teaspoon of the lime juice and pour it over the finished product, then cover with plastic wrap with the wrap touching the guacamole.

☐ Makes 8 servings.

*For a lower fat lighter version.

> **Per serving:** Calories 100, Protein 3 g., Fat 8 g., 63% fat (12% saturated fat), Carbohydrates 7 g., Dietary fiber 2 g., Cholesterol 1 mg., Sodium 91 mg., Calcium 66 mg., Iron 0.8 mg.
> **Exchanges:** vegetable 1 1/2; fat 1 1/2

HUMMUS

2 cups cooked garbanzo beans,
  drained, reserving liquid
2 tablespoons tahini (sesame paste)
Juice of one lemon

2 to 3 cloves of garlic, shoot
  removed and minced
1 teaspoon low sodium tamari
1/4 cup parsley, finely chopped

☐ Combine all ingredients in a food processor or blender and blend to a paste, add some of the reserved liquid if the mixture is too dry. Chill.

☐ Makes 2 cups.

☐ NOTE: Excellent as a dip with finger size pita bread triangles, or bite size vegetables; as a sandwich spread; as a substitute for sour cream in baked potatoes; or stuffed into cherry tomatoes, baby zucchini and/or celery boats. Also great as a pasta sauce if you heat the reserved liquid and add it just before tossing it with the pasta.

Variations:

*Add chopped lemon thyme, lemon balm, or lemon zest to enhance citrus flavors.
*Add chopped mint for a cool change.

*Add cumin and cayenne for a spicy touch.
*Add 1/2 cup nonfat plain yogurt for a lighter, lower fat version.

> **Per 1/4 cup serving:** Calories 118, Protein 6 g., Fat 4 g., 27% fat (3% saturated fat), Carbohydrates 17 g., Dietary fiber 2 g., Cholesterol 0 mg., Sodium 37 mg., Calcium 50 mg., Iron 2 mg.
> **Exchanges:** lean meat 1/2; bread 1; fat 1/2

EASY SPREADS AND MOUSSES

General Rules:
Use a ratio of 1:1 Yogurt Cheese (see page 34) to seafood or meat (these suggestions are proportioned for 1 cup, and the preparation will be referred to as "base"). Season to your tastes or theme. See the following for the flavor you would like to achieve.

Curry Variation

1 cup base (1/2 cup Yogurt Cheese plus 1/2 cup crab meat, finely chopped)
1 tablespoon lemon juice (or more to taste)
2 cloves garlic, shoot removed and mashed

1 to 2 teaspoons curry powder
1 teaspoon minced onion
1 teaspoon freshly ground cumin seeds
1 tablespoon fresh coriander, finely chopped

□ Mix all ingredients together, taste and adjust to your preference, then pipe onto cucumber slices, tiny toast triangles, crackers, or pita pocket triangles.

□ Makes 20 servings.

> **Per 1 tablespoon serving:** Calories 11, Protein 1 g., Fat trace, Carbohydrates 1 g., Dietary fiber trace, Cholesterol 3 mg., Sodium 17 mg., Calcium 28 mg., Iron trace.
> **Exchanges:** skim milk 1/2 per 1/4 cup serving

Mexican Variation

1 cup base (1/2 cup Yogurt Cheese plus 1/2 cup poached or leftover chicken, finely chopped)
1 tomatillo, finely chopped
1/2 ripe avocado, mashed
1 tablespoon fresh lime juice

1 inch piece of a jalapeño pepper, finely chopped (or a few dashes of hot sauce to taste)
1 tablespoon fresh coriander, finely chopped

□ Mix all ingredients together and serve with blue corn chips, burrito triangles, slices of jicama or stuffed into scooped out button mushrooms.

□ Makes 30 servings.

> **Per 1 tablespoon serving:** Calories 26, Protein 2 g.,
> Fat 1 g., 35% fat (7% saturated fat), Carbohydrates 2 g., Dietary fiber trace,
> Cholesterol 3 mg., Sodium 15 mg., Calcium 30 mg., Iron trace.
> **Exchanges:** lean meat, skim milk 1/2; fat 1/2 per 1/4 cup serving

CRISPY TURKEY NUGGETS

Nuggets

1¼ pound lean ground turkey
2 to 2½ cups grated precooked*
  potato
½ cup finely chopped scallions

2 tablespoons light soy sauce
1 tablespoon red wine vinegar
2 egg whites
½ cup dry curd cottage cheese

Coating

¾ cup sesame seeds
3 tablespoons oat bran

3 tablespoons grated part skim
  milk Parmesan cheese

☐ Combine all the ingredients for the nuggets and knead thoroughly to combine.

☐ Shape turkey mixture into 1½-inch nuggets.

☐ Combine the coating ingredients in a paper lunch bag, drop the nuggets into the coating 2 at a time and shake to coat.

☐ Place on a lightly oiled cookie sheet and bake in a preheated 425° F. oven for 30 minutes, turning after 15 minutes. Reduce heat to 350° F., cover loosely with foil and bake an additional 10 minutes. Serve hot with dipping sauce. Recipe follows.

☐ Makes 30 nuggets.

☐ *Place in steamer basket and steam for 5 minutes.

Per 1 nugget serving: Calories 58, Protein 5 g., Fat 3 g., 46% fat (* saturated fat),
Carbohydrates, 2 g., Dietary fiber 1 g., Cholesterol 13 mg., Sodium 52 mg.,
Calcium 43 mg., Iron 0.6 mg. *Data not available at this time.
Exchanges: lean meats 3; bread ½; fat 1 per 4 nuggets

Dipping Sauce

4 tablespoons ketchup
2 tablespoons Worcestershire sauce

½ cup tomato purée
Dash hot sauce

☐ Combine all ingredients and heat to boiling point.

☐ Makes 14 servings.

Per 1 tablespoon serving: Calories 11, Protein trace, Fat trace, Carbohydrates 2 g.,
Dietary fiber trace, Cholesterol 0 mg., Sodium 79 mg., Calcium 4 mg., Iron trace.
Exchanges: 1 tablespoon free

CRUDITE PLATTER WITH AN ASSORTMENT OF DIPS

Select a variety of seasonal vegetables such as broccoli, cauliflower, pea pods, beans, button mushrooms, zucchini, radishes, celery and fennel. Wash and trim them to bite-size pieces and arrange them attractively on a large platter. Remove the seeds from two bell peppers and · use them as containers for the dip.

Savory Blue Cheese Dip:

2 cups fat free cottage cheese
4 ounces crumbled blue cheese
2 tablespoons green onion, finely chopped
1 large clove garlic, shoot removed and finely minced

1 teaspoon Worcestershire sauce
2 tablespoons fresh lemon juice
1 cup nonfat plain yogurt
3 tablespoons fresh dill, finely chopped (1/2 teaspoon if using dry)

☐ Purée cottage cheese and blue cheese in food processor or blender.

☐ Add the onion, garlic, Worcestershire sauce, and lemon juice, pulse a couple of times to combine. Remove the mixture to a bowl and fold in the yogurt and dill.

☐ Makes 3 cups.

> **Per 1 tablespoon serving:** Calories 16, Protein 2 g., Fat 1 g., 39% fat (25% saturated fat), Carbohydrates 1 g., Dietary fiber trace, Cholesterol 2 mg., Sodium 68 mg., Calcium 25 mg., Iron trace.
> **Exchanges:** 1 tablespoon free; 2 tablespoons lean meat 1/2

Savory Salmon Dip: Omit the blue cheese, Worcestershire sauce, and dill. Follow the same directions substituting the following ingredients.

6 ounces fromage blanc
1 tablespoon curry powder
1 (61/2-ounce) can salmon packed in water, or fresh poached (broken up into small pieces), drained

1 teaspoon roasted ground coriander seeds
Season with salt and pepper as desired

☐ Makes 31/2 cups.

> **Per 1 tablespoon serving:** Calories 17, Protein 2 g., Fat trace, Carbohydrates 1 g., Dietary fiber trace, Cholesterol trace, Sodium 57 mg., Calcium 22 mg., Iron trace.
> **Exchanges:** 1 tablespoon free; 2 tablespoons lean meat 1/2

Beverages

MULLED APPLE CIDER

Great to warm up after cross country skiing!

1 gallon fresh apple cider
2 cinnamon sticks
2 cloves

¹/₄ of a whole nutmeg (about the size of a chickpea)

☐ Combine all ingredients in a large non-reactive pot such as enamel or stainless steel, and bring to a boil. Turn down the heat and simmer, partially covered, for 1 to 2 hours.

☐ Makes 21 (6-ounce) servings.

Per 1 (6-ounce) serving: Calories 71, Protein 0 g., Fat trace, 2% fat (trace saturated fat), Carbohydrates 18 g., Dietary fiber trace, Cholesterol 0 mg., Sodium 5 mg., Calcium 11 mg., Iron 0.6 mg.
Exchanges: fruit 1¹/₂

CRANBERRY PUNCH

1¹/₂ quarts low-calorie cranberry-raspberry juice, chilled
2 quarts raspberry-flavored seltzer water, chilled

1 (16-ounce) package frozen raspberries
Fresh fruit slices (orange, lemon, lime)

☐ Combine juice, seltzer water, and raspberries in a punch bowl. Garnish with fresh fruit slices or Ice Ring (page 112). Serve over ice.

☐ Makes 36 servings.

Per ¹/₂ cup serving: Calories 14, Protein trace, Fat trace, 0% fat (0% saturated fat), Carbohydrates 3 g., Dietary fiber 1 g., Cholesterol 0 mg., Sodium 1 mg., Calcium 6 mg., Iron trace.
Exchanges: 2 cups = fruit 1; ¹/₂ cup free

BANANA-CHOCOLATE SHAKE

10 ice cubes
1 tablespoon brown sugar (to taste)
1 ripe banana
1/2 cup nonfat yogurt

1/2 teaspoon chocolate extract
   (to taste)
Cocoa for garnish (optional)

☐ Best made just before serving.

☐ Process the ice cubes with the sugar in a blender until crushed. Add the remaining ingredients and process until light and fluffy.

☐ Pour into chilled glasses, sift a little cocoa on top (if desired) and serve.

☐ Makes 2 cups per serving.

Per 1 cup serving: Calories 110, Protein 4 g., Fat trace, Carbohydrates 24 g., Dietary fiber 1 g., Cholesterol 1 mg., Sodium 46 mg., Calcium 122 mg., Iron 0.5 mg.
Exchanges: fruit 1; skim milk 1/2 (Not recommended for diabetics)

PIQUANT AND FRUITY NON DAIRY SHAKE

2 cups fresh pineapple
2 cups fresh strawberries (1 pint)
1 Granny Smith apple, including
   the peel

1 12 ounce can concentrated
   frozen pure apple juice
8 ice cubes

☐ Combine all ingredients except the ice cubes in a blender and purée until smooth.

☐ Just before serving, add the ice cubes and purée again until they are crushed.

☐ Makes 8 (6-ounce) servings.

Variations: For a lighter drink, cut half the volume with seltzer water. Vary the fruit according to what is in season such as: peaches and apples, kiwi and banana, and papaya and passionfruit. Coordinate the fruit juice to complement the fruit.

Per 1 (6-ounce) serving: Calories 129, Protein 1 g., Fat 1 g., 4% fat (trace saturated fat), Carbohydrates 32 g., Dietary fiber 3 g., Cholesterol 0 mg., Sodium 14 mg., Calcium 20 mg., Iron 0.8 mg.
Exchanges: fruit 2 1/2

SALADS & SOUPS

Gail's Fresh Artichoke and Tomato Salad
page 47

Grilled Pork Tenderloin
page 95

Easy Rice Pilaf
page 107

Honey Whole Wheat Bread
with Walnuts
page 62

Blackberry Sorbet
page 138

Per serving for complete menu: Calories 713, Protein 45 g., Fat 18 g. (total = 23% saturated = 4%), Carbohydrates 93 g., Dietary fiber 14 g., Cholesterol 106 mg., Sodium 808 mg., Calcium 170 mg., Iron 7 mg.

Salads are a great accompaniment to a main course or they can stand alone as lunch or a light supper. They are alive with texture and flavor. We encourage you to build your own salads with what's available either in your supermarket or garden. The sky's the limit!

Photograph: Gail's Fresh Artichoke and Tomato Salad, Spicy Autumn Harvest Soup, pages 47 and 51

GAIL'S FRESH ARTICHOKE AND TOMATO SALAD

1 cup water
1/2 cup dry white wine
2 tablespoons extra virgin olive oil
3 thin lemon slices (1/4 of a lemon)
2 cloves of garlic, flattened but left
  whole and unpeeled
2 thyme sprigs (or 1/4 teaspoon dry)
2 bay leaves

1 teaspoon salt (optional)
12 whole black peppercorns
6 coriander seeds
12 baby artichokes (use 4 large or 6
  medium) or 20 ounces frozen
  artichoke hearts
10 ounces button mushrooms,
  wiped clean

☐ Place all the ingredients (except the artichokes and mushrooms) into a large pot and bring to a boil.

☐ Remove the outer leaves of the artichokes, snapping them back as you go, to avoid discarding any of the heart. Cut the artichokes in half (if large) and add them to the boiling water, return to a boil. Reduce the heat, cover and simmer until tender, about 15 minutes for babies, 20 minutes for large, or 5 minutes for frozen hearts.

☐ Remove artichokes and set aside. Return the cooking liquid to the boil, and add the mushrooms, bring back to a boil, cover and simmer for 5 minutes. Remove from heat and allow to cool in liquid. Drain, reserving 1/2 cup of the cooking liquid. Halve artichokes through stem end, and remove any choke (the furry stuff and tough inner leaves) with a spoon or melon baller. Cut the hearts into bite-size pieces and set aside. This can be done a day in advance.

Dressing

2 tablespoons fresh lemon juice
2 cloves of garlic, minced (shoot
  removed)

1 tablespoon tomato purée
1/2 cup reserved cooking liquid
2 tablespoons extra virgin olive oil

☐ Place all ingredients in jar and shake vigorously.

Salad

4 ripe tomatoes, squeezed of excess
  juice and diced

Lettuce leaves for garnish

☐ Place the above ingredients along with the artichoke hearts in a large bowl, pour the dressing over them and toss well. Allow to marinate at room temperature for at least 1 hour. Serve on a bed of lettuce.

☐ Makes 8 servings. (photo page 45)

Per serving: Calories 151, Protein 5 g., Fat 7 g., 42% fat (6% saturated fat),
  Carbohydrates 18 g., Dietary fiber 2 g., Cholesterol 0 mg., Sodium 356 mg.,
  Calcium 71 mg., Iron 2.8 mg.
Exchanges: vegetable 4; fat 1

GAZPACHO SALAD

4 large tomatoes, diced
1/2 green pepper, seeds removed
  and diced
1/2 red pepper, seeds removed and
  diced
8 scallions, finely chopped
1 bunch fresh parsley, thoroughly
  washed and finely chopped

6 mushrooms, wiped clean and
  sliced
1 clove of garlic, shoot removed,
  mashed
1 teaspoon salt (optional)
1/2 cup freshly squeezed lemon juice
1/2 cup ice water
Dash hot pepper sauce

☐ In a large bowl combine the tomatoes, green and red peppers, scallions, parsley and mushrooms. Combine the garlic, salt, lemon juice, water and hot sauce. Pour over the vegetables and toss to combine, taste and adjust seasonings as desired.

☐ Makes 8 servings.

Per serving: Calories 25, Protein 1 g., Fat trace, Carbohydrates 6 g., Dietary fiber 1 g., Cholesterol 0 mg., Sodium 142 mg., Calcium 21 mg., Iron 1.1 mg.
Exchanges: vegetable 1

BROCCOLI MUSHROOM BULGUR SALAD

1 head of broccoli flowerettes,
  blanched (5 to 6 cups)
2 tablespoons sugar
1/2 teaspoon salt (optional)
1 teaspoon each paprika, celery
  seeds and onion powder
2 tablespoon olive oil
1 tablespoon low sodium soy sauce

5 to 6 tablespoons cider or wine
  vinegar (or your favorite vinegar)
1 teaspoon *Better than Bouillon
  vegetable base (optional)
1 cup bulgur (cracked wheat)
1 pound mushrooms, thinly sliced
  (6 to 7 cups)
1/2 cup shredded green onion tops

☐ Blanch the broccoli flowerettes in rapidly boiling water until they become bright green, refrigerate immediately to set their color. Reserve 1 1/2 cups of the broccoli water. Combine the next 9 ingredients with the reserved broccoli water and heat to boiling. Pour over the bulgur and allow to sit at least 2 hours or overnight.

☐ Toss with the mushrooms and broccoli. Heap into an attractive serving dish and sprinkle with the shredded green onion tops for garnish.

☐ Makes 10 servings (10 to 11 cups).

*Better than Bouillon Vegetable Base is available at specialty food stores and co-ops. You can substitute your favorite vegetable or chicken seasoning.

Per 1 cup serving: Calories 98, Protein 4 g., Fat 3 g. (28%), Carbohydrates 16 g., Dietary fiber 6 g., Cholestersol 0 mg., Sodium 167 mg., Calcium 37 mg., Iron 1.5 mg.
Exchanges: bread 1/2; vegetable 1; fat 1

REFRESHING WILD RICE ALL SEASON'S SALAD

2 cups cooked wild rice (made from
  1 cup raw)
2 cups cooked brown rice (made
  from 1 cup raw)
2 medium carrots, diced
2 ribs celery, diced
2 green onions, thinly sliced
1 cup broccoli flowerettes, blanched

2 tablespoons olive oil
2 tablespoons low-sodium soy sauce
2 tablespoons red wine vinegar
Dash of black pepper
1 clove of garlic, shoot removed
  and mashed
1/2 teaspoon freshly grated ginger
Dash of hot sauce

☐ Place all of the ingredients into a bowl, toss well and allow to marinate for 2 hours. Serve on a bed of kale, red cabbage or some attractive greens to complement the salad.

☐ Makes 6 servings.

Microwave Cooking Directions for the Rice

☐ These can be cooked together in your microwave.

☐ In a 2¹/2 to 3 quart casserole dish, combine the rice with ¹/2 teaspoon salt (optional) and 4 cups of cold water.

☐ Cook 12 minutes on High then 30 minutes on Simmer. If all the water is not absorbed by the end of the cooking time, cook an additional 5 to 10 minutes.

Per Serving: Calories 216, Protein 4 g., Fat 5 g., 21% fat (2% saturated fat),
  Carbohydrates 38 g., Dietary fiber 6 g., Cholesterol 0 mg., Sodium 232 mg.,
  Calcium 20 mg., Iron 0.9 mg.
Exchanges: bread 2; vegetable 1; fat 1

TOSSED WINTER SALAD WITH RASPBERRY VINAIGRETTE

6 ounces greens such as spinach or
  romaine lettuce (after sorting)
¹/2 cup julienned red pepper
¹/2 cup julienned carrot

¹/2 cup seedless grapes, cut in half
2 tablespoons slivered almonds,
  lightly toasted

☐ Sort and cut all the ingredients and toss with ¹/4 cup Raspberry Vinaigrette (page 50), just before serving.

☐ Makes 6 servings.

Per serving: Calories 67, Protein 1 g., Fat 5 g., 67% fat (7% saturated fat),
  Carbohydrates 6 g., Dietary fiber 2 g., Cholesterol 0 mg., Sodium 18 mg.,
  Calcium 28 mg., Iron 0.7 mg.
Exchanges: vegetable 1; fat 1

INDIVIDUAL FRUIT SALADS WITH LIME-GINGER DRESSING

Lettuce leaves to line 6 plates
(2 to a plate if small)
12 to 18 ripe strawberries, cut
towards their stems 2 to 3 times
and fanned
2 kiwifruits, peeled and sliced

$^{1}/_{2}$ small ripe melon, scooped into
balls
2 to 3 navel oranges, peeled and
sliced
Lime Ginger Dressing

☐ Line each plate with lettuce. Arrange the fruit attractively on the lettuce. Drizzle each with 2 teaspoons dressing.

☐ Can be assembled up to an hour ahead of time.

☐ Makes 6 servings.

Lime Ginger Dressing
Juice of 2 limes
1 clove of garlic, shoot removed
and mashed
$^{1}/_{2}$ teaspoon freshly ground fresh
ginger

$^{1}/_{2}$ teaspoon Dijon-style mustard
$^{1}/_{3}$ cup virgin olive oil
1 tablespoon fresh herb of choice,
such as tarragon, rosemary or
basil finely chopped (optional)

☐ Combine all ingredients in a jar and shake vigorously until well mixed.

> Per serving: Calories 132, Protein 2 g., Fat 6 g., 41% fat (6% saturated fat),
> Carbohydrates 19 g., Dietary fiber 3 g., Cholesterol 0 mg., Sodium 13 mg.,
> Calcium 53 mg., Iron 0.6 mg.
> Exchanges: fruit 1; fat 1

RASPBERRY VINAIGRETTE

$^{1}/_{2}$ to 1 teaspoon honey
$^{1}/_{4}$ cup Raspberry Vinegar
(page 67)
$^{1}/_{4}$ cup olive oil

2 cloves of garlic, shoot removed
and mashed
Pinch of salt (optional)

☐ Combine all ingredients in a jar and shake vigorously. This is great tossed with a mixed green salad. Makes $^{1}/_{2}$ cup.

> Per 2 teaspoons serving: Calories 42, Protein 0 g.,
> Fat 5 g., 100% fat (13% saturated fat), Carbohydrates 1 g., Dietary fiber 0 g.,
> Cholesterol 0 mg., Sodium 0 mg., Calcium 1 mg., Iron trace.
> Exchanges: fat 1

Soups

SPICY AUTUMN HARVEST SOUP

1 medium onion, chopped
1 teaspoon olive oil
2 cloves of garlic, chopped
1/2 teaspoon ground cinnamon
1/4 teaspoon grated fresh ginger
1/4 teaspoon ground coriander seeds
1/4 teaspoon ground cumin seeds
1/8 teaspoon ground turmeric
2 cups apple cider
1 medium to large butternut
  squash, peeled and coarsely
  chopped

2 large cooking apples peeled,
  seeded and coarsely chopped
3 cups low-sodium *chicken stock
  (defatted if canned)
1/2 cup nonfat plain yogurt
1/4 cup sliced almonds, lightly
  roasted

☐ In a 3 to 4-quart heavy saucepan sauté the onions in the olive oil until wilted, add the garlic and spices, stir well.

☐ Add the remaining ingredients and bring to the boil, turn down the heat and simmer for 2 to 3 hours or until the apples and squash are tender, then purée in the blender until smooth. Reheat before serving. Garnish each individual serving with a dollop of yogurt and a sprinkling of toasted sliced almonds.

☐ Makes eight 1-cup servings. (photo page 45)

☐ *To de-fat canned chicken stock, chill it before opening. The fat solidifies when chilled and can be easily removed by straining.

☐ NOTE: For a quick version omit the individual spices and use 1 to 2 teaspoons curry powder. If consistency is too thick, add more chicken stock.

Per 1 cup serving: Calories 125, Protein 4 g., Fat 3 g., 19% fat (2% saturated fat),
  Carbohydrates 24 g., Dietary fiber 3 g., Cholesterol trace, Sodium 16 mg.,
  Calcium 80 mg., Iron 1 mg.
Exchanges: fruit 1; bread 1/2; fat 1/2; vegetable 1

MIDDLE EASTERN STYLE RED LENTIL SOUP

1 teaspoon canola oil
3 medium onions, diced
  (approximately 3 cups)
3 cloves garlic, minced
2 teaspoons fresh grated ginger
1/2 teaspoon vegit seasoning
  (or your favorite vegetarian
  seasoning)

1 teaspoon ground coriander*
1 teaspoon ground cumin*
1 cup red lentils, thoroughly washed
4 cups water
1 (15-ounce) can tomato sauce
  (no added salt)
1/2 teaspoon salt, optional
  (calculated into recipe)

☐ Sauté onions in oil over medium-low heat until transparent. Add garlic and cook a further 5 minutes, taking care not to burn it. Add fresh ginger, vegit seasoning and spices, stir 1 to 2 minutes. Add water and lentils and bring to a boil. Lower the heat and simmer for 30 to 45 minutes or until lentils are tender. Add tomato sauce, reheat and serve.

☐ Makes 6 cups.

☐ NOTE: *For optimum flavor, it is best to buy spices whole (in small amounts so they stay fresh) and grind them in a mortar and pestle just before adding them to the recipe.

Per 1 cup serving: Calories 185, Protein 12 g., Fat 2 g., 8% fat (1% saturated fat), Carbohydrates 34 g., Dietary fiber 5 g., Cholesterol 0 mg., Sodium 196 mg., Calcium 34 mg., Iron 4 mg.
Exchanges: vegetable 1; bread 2; lean meat 1/2

PURÉE OF LEEK AND POTATO SOUP

1 tablespoon canola oil
2 stalks celery, diced
5 cups leeks, diced
1 large onion, diced

4 cups potatoes, peeled and chopped
2 quarts defatted* low-sodium
  chicken stock
Freshly ground black pepper to taste

☐ Heat canola oil in a 5-quart heavy-duty pot. Add leeks, celery and onion and sauté until translucent and soft, about 10 minutes. Add potatoes and chicken stock, cover and bring to a boil. Reduce heat and simmer for 30 to 40 minutes, or until potatoes are soft. Purée vegetables with some of the broth in a food processor or blender until smooth. Taste and add freshly ground pepper to taste. If you are using homemade chicken stock (without added salt) you may need to add up to 1 teaspoon salt. Reheat and serve.

☐ NOTE: *To defat chicken stock, refrigerate and strain to remove the solidified fat.

☐ Makes 9 cups.

Per 1 cup serving: Calories 232, Protein 3 g., Fat 2 g., 14% fat (1% saturated fat), Carbohydrates 24 g., Dietary fiber 2 g., Cholesterol 0 mg., Sodium 33 mg., Calcium 110 mg., Iron 2 mg.
Exchanges: bread 1; fat 1/2; vegetable 1

MICHIGAN BLACK BEAN SOUP

1½ cups black beans, washed,
  sorted and soaked 4 hours or
  overnight
6 cups water
1 cup diced carrots
1 cup diced celery
1 medium onion, coarsely chopped
2 cloves of garlic, chopped

2 dashes angostura bitters
  (optional)
1 tablespoon barley miso or 2
  tablespoons low-sodium soy sauce
1 teaspoon dark corn syrup
Dash hot sauce
½ teaspoon salt

☐ Drain beans, discarding their soaking water. Place the beans in a heavy duty 3-quart saucepan, add 6 cups of fresh water and bring to a boil. Lower the heat and simmer for 30 minutes. Add the remaining ingredients and continue to simmer 30 minutes or until the beans are tender.

☐ Purée in batches in a blender until smooth, adjust seasonings, reheat and serve.

☐ Makes 8 cups.

Per 1 cup serving: Calories 149, Protein 9 g., Fat 1 g., 6% fat (1% saturated fat),
  Carbohydrates 28 g., Dietary fiber 8 g., Cholesterol 0 mg., Sodium 251 mg.,
  Calcium 65 mg., Iron 2 mg.
Exchanges: bread 1½; vegetable 1

TWO-TONE PEAR RASPBERRY SOUP

This fruity and visually stunning soup is excellent as an appetizer or palate cleanser.

1 (12-ounce) package frozen
  raspberries, thawed
½ cup frozen concentrated
  cranberry-raspberry juice

4 ripe pears
1 teaspoon grated fresh ginger
1 tablespoon lemon juice

☐ Sieve the raspberries to remove their seeds, and combine with the cranberry-raspberry juice. Refrigerate at least an hour before serving.

☐ Peel and core the pears, purée with the grated ginger and lemon juice. Refrigerate at least an hour before serving.

☐ To serve, pour both purées simultaneously into small serving dishes (crystal looks good), adding slightly more pear than raspberry. With a spoon or fork, swirl one end of the pear into the raspberry, it will resemble a swan shape.

☐ Makes 6 servings.

Per serving: Calories 108, Protein 1 g., Fat 1 g., 8% fat (trace saturated fat),
  Carbohydrates 27 g., Dietary fiber 6 g., Cholesterol 0 mg., Sodium 1 mg.,
  Calcium 25 mg., Iron 0.6 mg.
Exchanges: fruit 2

CAULIFLOWER MUSHROOM BISQUE

1 head cauliflower, broken into
  flowerettes (7 to 8 cups)
1 medium onion, diced (1 to 1½ cups)
½ teaspoon olive oil
1 clove of garlic, finely chopped

6 ounces mushrooms, sliced (2 cups)
1 (15-ounce) can Great Northern
  beans, including the liquid
1 teaspoon salt (optional)
Fresh parsley for garnish

☐ Steam cauliflower in 3 cups of boiling water until tender (6 to 8 minutes), reserve water. Over moderate heat, sauté onions in olive oil until transparent, about 5 minutes, add garlic and sauté for a few minutes. Remove and set aside. Turn up heat, add mushrooms, and sauté until they begin to wilt. Combine cauliflower, onions, garlic and beans in blender. Add enough of the reserved cauliflower water to purée until smooth. May divide into 2 or 3 batches. Return the puréed mixture and any remaining cauliflower water to mushrooms and reheat. Add salt if desired. Garnish with parsley.

☐ Makes 8 cups.

Per 1 cup serving: Calories 103, Protein 7 g., Fat 1 g., 7% fat (1% saturated fat), Carbohydrates 20 g., Dietary fiber 6 g., Cholesterol 0 mg., Sodium 284 mg., Calcium 64 mg., Iron 2 mg.
Exchanges: vegetable 1; bread 1

GINGERED CARROT SOUP

½ teaspoon olive oil
1 onion, diced (½ cup)
1 clove garlic, shoot removed and
  mashed
1 pound carrots, diced
  (3 heaping cups)
2 tablespoons heaping raw white
  rice (1½ ounces)

½ teaspoon ginger root, freshly grated
3 (14½-ounce) cans clear chicken
  broth, low sodium, fat free
2 ounces frozen concentrated
  orange juice
½ cup evaporated skim milk
7 teaspoons nonfat plain yogurt
  (optional garnish)

☐ Heat olive oil in a large heavy saucepan. Add onion and garlic, sauté for 5 minutes. Add carrots, continue to sauté until carrots release juices. Add rice and ginger root, continue to sauté a few more minutes. Pour in chicken stock, bring to a boil. Turn down heat and simmer until rice is cooked and carrots are tender, about 30 minutes. Purée in a blender until smooth, add concentrated orange juice and skim milk and reheat. Serve, garnished with 1 teaspoon of nonfat yogurt swirled into the soup.

☐ Makes 7 cups.

Per 1 cup serving: Calories 105, Protein 5 g., Fat 2 g., 15% fat (1% saturated fat), Carbohydrates 17 g., Dietary fiber 2 g., Cholesterol 1 mg., Sodium 93 mg., Calcium 94 mg., Iron 1 mg.
Exchanges: vegetable 2; bread ½

BREADS

Gazpacho Salad with Breadsticks
page 48 and 57

Fettuccini with Scallops and Mussels
page 91

Poached Pears with Hazelnut Custard

page 131

Per serving for complete menu: Calories, 817, Protein 36 g.,
Fat 16 g. (total = 18% saturated *), Carbohydrates 127 g.,
Dietary fiber 9 g., Cholesterol 55 mg., Sodium 844 mg.,
Calcium 383 mg., Iron 12.3 mg. *Data not available at this time.

We include yeast breads, quick breads and muffins in this chapter. Baking your own yeast bread can be highly relaxing, even a pleasantly sensual experience. The aromas of bread rising, and then baking in the oven conjure up pleasant memories of visits to Grandmother in our youth, and the hands-on kneading of the dough is a delightful experience in our convenience-food automated world. For helpful information to make your bread-baking experience easier, refer to *The Joy of Cooking* bread section.

Photograph: Crusty Rolls with Whole Grains and Oat Bran, High Fit - Low Fat Breadsticks, Cranberry Nut Bread, Crusty Whole Wheat Braids, Honey Whole Grain Blueberry Muffins, pages 55, 57, 60 and 61

HIGH FIT - LOW FAT BREADSTICKS

This recipe will convert into French Baguettes, as will any of the other bread recipes convert into breadsticks. It's all in the rolling and cooking. However, the extra yeast and contradictory method of combining these ingredients give these bread sticks a distinctive flavor.

2 tablespoons (scant) yeast
2 teaspoons sugar
1 teaspoon salt
1 tablespoon olive oil
2 cups water (104° to 115° F.)

4 to 5 cups bread flour (or 3 cups
    white and 2¹/₂ cups whole wheat)
1 egg white, beaten
1 tablespoon water
Sesame seeds or poppy seeds

☐ Combine the yeast, sugar, salt, olive oil and ¹/₄ cup of water and beat with a whisk or wooden spoon for about 3 minutes.

☐ Add the remaining water and flour alternately (reserving ¹/₂ cup of flour for kneading), beating vigorously with the wooden spoon until you have a soft dough.

☐ Remove the dough to a floured surface, and knead until smooth and elastic (so that it springs back when depressed with the fingers) about 5 to 6 minutes.

☐ Let the dough rest, covered with a towel, for 5 minutes, then shape it into a roll about 2 feet long. With a dough scraper or sharp knife, cut the dough into 18 equal pieces. Rest the dough an additional 3 minutes, then roll each piece with the palms of your hands against the counter until the strands are long enough to make two 12-inch bread rolls, or cut them to the length of your preference. Place on a lightly greased cookie sheet that has been sprinkled with poppy seeds or sesame seeds.

☐ Allow them to rest, covered, for 20 minutes or until they just begin to rise. Combine egg white and water, brush over breadsticks and sprinkle with sesame seeds or poppy seeds. Bake in a preheated 300° F. oven for 30 minutes. Turn up the oven to 400° F. and bake an additional 5 to 10 minutes or until they are crisp and golden brown.

☐ If using this dough for baguettes, be sure to bake them at 400° F. You should get 4 moderate size loaves.

☐ Makes 36 breadsticks. These will retain their crispness for several days if kept in an airtight container. (photo page 55)

Per 1 breadstick serving: Calories 59, Protein 2 g., Fat 1 g., 15% fat (1% saturated fat),
  Carbohydrates 11 g., Dietary fiber 1 g., Cholesterol 0 mg., Sodium 120 mg.,
  Calcium 4 mg., Iron 0.4 mg.
Exchanges: bread 1.

• You can create your own heat and humidity to hasten the rising process. Erect a tent of plastic, such as a large garbage bag, over sink of hot water in which you have placed a bowl of dough. Replace the hot water as it cools.

HEARTY MIXED GRAIN BREAD

*If you use the yogurt whey for these loaves, they develop an interesting almost sourdough
flavor. Either way they are hearty and deliciously chewy.*

1/3 cup boiling water	2 cups whole wheat bread flour
1/2 cup bulgar	1 cup barley flour
2 1/2 cups yogurt whey (or you can	1 cup oat bran
substitute water) 104° to 115° F.	2 cups white bread flour
1 tablespoon yeast	1 egg white, beaten
1 cup oatmeal	1 tablespoon water
2 tablespoons olive oil	Sesame seeds (optional)
2 teaspoons salt (optional)	

☐ Pour the boiling water over the bulgar and allow to soak for 15 minutes; set aside.

☐ Combine the yogurt whey or water with the yeast and oatmeal, wait 5 minutes to be
sure there is activity such as bubbles which indicate that the yeast is alive. Add the
oil and salt if desired, then add the whole wheat flour, barley flour, oat bran, soaked
bulgar and 1 1/2 cups of the white flour stirring vigorously after each addition.

☐ Turn the dough out onto a floured surface and knead until smooth and elastic, adding
small quantities of the reserved flour as necessary or until the dough is no longer
sticky.*

☐ Return the dough to a lightly oiled bowl, cover and place in a dark, warm draft-free
place to rise until doubled in bulk.** This may take 1 to 2 hours depending on heat
and humidity. (You can create your own heat and humidity to hasten this process by
erecting a tent of plastic, such as a large garbage bag, over a sink of hot water in which
you have placed the bowl of dough. Replace the hot water as it cools off.)

☐ When the dough has doubled, turn out of the bowl, and punch down. Divide the dough
into equal portions and shape into braids or rolls. You should expect to get 4 medium
regular or braided loaves or 50 dinner rolls (1 1/2 ounces of dough). Place dough on
cookie sheet (lightly sprinkled with cornmeal) and allow to rise, covered, until
doubled again. Combine egg white and water. Brush dough with egg mixture and
sprinkle with sesame seeds if desired. Bake in a preheated 400° F. oven for 20 to 35
minutes. Remove from the oven, turn onto racks to cool. These loaves freeze well.

☐ Makes 50 dinner rolls or 4 medium loaves.

Per serving (per roll): Calories 66, Protein 2 g., Fat 1 g., 14% fat (1% saturated fat),
  Carbohydrates 12 g., Dietary fiber 1 g., Cholesterol 0 mg., Sodium 86 mg.,
  Calcium 4 mg., Iron 0.4 mg.
Exchanges: bread 1

• The dough has been kneaded sufficiently when it is no longer sticky, it should
spring back when depressed with the fingers.

• The dough has doubled in bulk when it collapses inwards when depressed
with the fingers.

LIGHT AND FLUFFY POTATO BREAD WITH OAT BRAN

You'll love the interesting sourdough flavor.

1 tablespoon yeast
8¹/₂ to 9 cups white bread flour
2 cups oat bran
¹/₂ cup rice flour
4 cups potato water*
1 tablespoon salt

¹/₄ cup canola oil
Vegetable cooking spray
Cornmeal
1 egg white, beaten
1 tablespoon water

☐ Place the yeast, ¹/₂ of the bread flour, all of the oat bran and rice flour in a large mixing bowl with all of the water. Whisk until well combined. Leave this mixture a few minutes until you see some yeast activity (i.e. bubbles).

☐ Add the salt and oil, mix well. Gradually add enough of the remaining white flour until the mixture cleans the sides of the bowl.

☐ Turn the dough out onto a lightly floured surface and knead until smooth and elastic, adding small quantities of the reserved flour as necessary or until the dough is no longer sticky.

Return the dough to a clean lightly oiled bowl, cover and place in a dark, warm, draft-free place to rise until doubled in bulk. This may take 1 to 2 hours depending on heat and humidity.

☐ When the dough has doubled, turn out of the bowl, and punch down. Return to the bowl and repeat rising procedure until doubled. This should happen more quickly than the first time. Lightly grease the cover, particularly during the final rising. An opened out garbage bag works well as a cover and can be re-used many times. You can omit the second rising if time does not permit. The texture will be a little more coarse and dense.

☐ Divide the dough into equal portions and shape into braids or rolls. The best way to get an even yield is to weigh the dough on a scale. You should expect to get 4 large braids or 40 dinner rolls (2 ounces dough). Place on cookie sheet sprayed with vegetable cooking spray and sprinkled with cornmeal. Allow to rise, covered, until doubled again. Combine egg white and water and brush over loaves if desired. Bake in a preheated 400° F. oven for 20 to 35 minutes. Remove from the oven, turn onto racks to cool.

☐ *Water in which about 2 pounds of potatoes have been cooked. May use the whey from making yogurt cheese instead of the potato water.

☐ Makes 4 large, 6 medium braided loaves or 40 dinner rolls.

☐ NOTE: To hasten the yeast activity in step 1, add 1 teaspoon molasses, honey or sugar. To reduce the fat content omit the oil if you are going to eat the bread the same day, the main purpose of the oil is to improve the shelf life. Decrease the flour accordingly.

Per 1 slice or roll serving: (Allow 10 slices per loaf) Calories 82, Protein 3 g.,
Fat 1 g., 11% fat (1% saturated fat), Carbohydrates 14 g., Dietary fiber 1 g.,
Cholesterol 0 mg., Sodium 108 mg., Calcium 3 mg., Iron 0.5 mg.
Exchanges: bread 1

WHOLE GRAIN BLUEBERRY-APPLE MUFFINS

1 1/2 cups all-purpose flour
1/2 cup oat bran
1/2 cup wheat bran (or All Bran)
1/2 cup whole wheat flour
1 tablespoon baking powder
2 teaspoons cinnamon

1/2 cup brown sugar
1 cup chunky apple sauce
1 cup apple cider (or juice)
2 tablespoons canola oil
2 egg whites
1 cup blueberries (fresh or frozen)

Topping (optional)
2 tablespoons oatmeal

1 tablespoon brown sugar

☐ Combine dry ingredients. Combine all liquid ingredients and add them to the dry, mix to incorporate. Fold in blueberries. Mix the topping ingredients together and sprinkle on top of the muffins. Bake in the center of a preheated 400° F. oven for approximately 20 minutes, or until a toothpick inserted into the center of a muffin comes out clean.

☐ Makes 12 muffins.

Per 1 muffin serving: Calories 176, Protein 4 g., Fat 3 g., 13% fat (1% saturated fat), Carbohydrates 37 g., Dietary fiber 3 g., Cholesterol 0 mg., Sodium 139 mg., Calcium 40 mg., Iron 2 mg.
Exchanges: fruit 1 1/2; bread 1; fat 1/2 (Not recommended for diabetics)

OAT BRAN PUMPKIN MUFFINS

2 1/2 cups oatmeal
3/4 cup oat bran
1/2 cup cooked mashed pumpkin
1/3 cup brown sugar*
1 cup apple cider
2 egg whites

1 tablespoon canola oil
1 tablespoon baking powder
1/2 teaspoon baking soda
1 teaspoon pumpkin pie spice
1 1/2 teaspoons cinnamon
1 cup prunes (or dried fruit of choice)

☐ Grind oatmeal and oat bran together in the food processor or blender until the consistency of coarse flour. Combine the liquid ingredients, mix well to dissolve the sugar. Combine the spices and leavenings and add them to the dry ingredients. Fold the oat bran/oatmeal mixture into the liquid ingredients and stir only to integrate ingredients. Fold in the prunes or dried fruit of choice. Ladle into muffin tins and bake in preheated 400° F. oven for 15 to 20 minutes. Cool on racks.

☐ Makes 12 muffins.

Per 1 muffin serving: Calories 168, Protein 5 g., Fat 3 g., 16% fat (2% saturated fat), Carbohydrates 35 g., Dietary fiber 3 g., Cholesterol 0 mg., Sodium 133 mg., Calcium 87 mg., Iron 2 mg.
Exchanges: fruit 1/2; bread 1 1/2; fat 1/2 (Not recommended for diabetics

CRUSTY WHOLE WHEAT BRAIDS

When braided, these loaves are festive in appearance and easy to serve as they have a natural cleavage point at each braid and do not need to be cut. They can also be shaped into 3 dozen dinner rolls if preferred.

2 packages dry yeast (2 tablespoons)
9 to 9¹/₂ cups whole wheat bread
   flour
2 teaspoons honey
4 cups water (105° to 115° F.)
1 tablespoon salt (optional)

¹/₃ cup canola oil
Vegetable cooking spray
Cornmeal
1 egg white, beaten
1 tablespoon water
2 tablespoons sesame seeds

☐ Place the yeast, ¹/₂ of the flour and the honey in a large mixing bowl with all of the water. Whisk until well combined. Leave this mixture a few minutes until some yeast activity (i.e. bubbles) is visible.

☐ Add the salt if desired and oil, mix well. Gradually add enough of the remaining flour until the mixture cleans the sides of the bowl.

☐ Turn the dough out onto a lightly floured surface and knead until smooth and elastic adding small quantities of the reserved flour as necessary.

☐ Return the dough to a lightly oiled bowl, cover and place in a dark, warm, draft-free place to rise until doubled in bulk. This may take 1 to 2 hours depending on heat and humidity.

☐ When the dough has doubled, turn out of the bowl and punch down. Return to bowl to rise until doubled. This should happen more quickly than the first time. You can omit the second rising if time does not permit. The texture will be a little more coarse and dense.

☐ Divide the dough into 4 equal portions and shape for rolls or braids. Place on cookie sheets that have been sprayed with vegetable cooking spray and sprinkled with cornmeal. Allow to rise, covered, until doubled again. Combine egg white and water, brush over dough then sprinkle with sesame seeds and bake in a preheated 400° F. oven for 20 to 35 minutes (20 minutes for rolls, closer to 35 for loaves). During the first 15 minutes of baking, mist the oven at regular intervals (at least twice) with a spray bottle of water. Remove from the oven, turn loaves onto racks to cool.

☐ Makes 4 loaves, 18 slices per loaf. These loaves freeze well. (photo page 55)

Per 1 slice serving: Calories 139, Protein 4 g., Fat 3 g., 20% fat (1% saturated fat),
   Carbohydrates 24 g., Dietary fiber 3 g., Cholesterol 0 mg., Sodium 180 mg.,
   Calcium 13 mg., Iron 0.6 mg.
Exchanges: bread 1¹/₂; fat ¹/₂

• Water too hot will kill the yeast, and water too cold will shock it. Either way you could spoil your bread.

• An opened out garbage bag works well as a cover and can be reused many times.)

HONEY WHOLE WHEAT BREAD WITH WALNUTS

4 cups warm water (105° to 115° F.)
1½ tablespoons yeast
2 tablespoons honey
4 cups whole wheat bread flour
1 cup oat bran
⅓ cup plus 2 tablespoons canola oil
1 tablespoon salt

1 cup oat bran
4 to 5 cups white bread flour
1 cup walnuts or pecans, chopped
1 cup raisins
Vegetable cooking spray
Cornmeal
1 egg white, beaten (optional)
1 tablespoon water (optional)

☐ Combine the water, yeast and honey and wait until activity is visible (i.e. bubbles), then add the whole wheat flour and oat bran.

☐ Add the oil and salt; mix well. Gradually add enough of the remaining flour until the mixture cleans the sides of the bowl.

☐ Turn the dough out onto a lightly floured surface and knead in the nuts and raisins. Continue to knead until smooth and elastic, adding small quantities of the reserved flour as necessary.

☐ Return the dough to a clean, lightly oiled bowl, cover, and place in a dark, warm, draft-free place to rise until doubled in bulk. This may take 1 to 2 hours depending on heat and humidity.

☐ When the dough has doubled, turn out of the bowl and punch down. Return to bowl and repeat rising until doubled. This should happen more quickly than the first time. Lightly grease the cover, particularly during the final rising. An opened-out garbage bag works well as a cover and can be used many times. You can omit the second rising if time does not permit. The texture will be a little more coarse and dense.

☐ Divide the dough into 4 equal portions and shape for loaves. Place in loaf pans sprayed with vegetable cooking spray and sprinkled with cornmeal. Allow to rise, covered, until doubled again. Bake in a preheated 400° F. oven for 35 minutes. Remove from the oven turn loaves onto racks to cool. Combine egg white and water and brush over loaves before baking if desired.

☐ Makes 4 loaves (18 slices per loaf).

☐ NOTE: This bread makes excellent toast. Leave out the raisins and nuts and reduce the honey to 1 tablespoon for a plain loaf for sandwiches. Freezes well.

Per 1 slice serving: Calories 81, Protein 2 g., Fat 2 g., 22% fat (1% saturated fat), Carbohydrates 13 g., Dietary fiber 1 g., Cholesterol 0 mg., Sodium 100 mg., Calcium 4 mg., Iron 0.4 mg.
Exchanges: bread 1

• The bread is cooked when tapping its bottom yields hollow sound.

• To store bread, freeze it sealed tightly in a plastic bag, (if you want to keep it fresh beyond two days). If it takes you several days to eat a whole loaf, cut it into slices before freezing and use as needed.

CRUSTY ROLLS WITH WHOLE GRAINS AND OAT BRAN

1¹/2 tablespoons yeast
4 cups white bread flour
4 cups warm water (105° to 115° F.)
¹/4 cup canola oil
1 tablespoon salt
1 cup oat bran

6¹/2 cups whole wheat bread flour
Vegetable cooking spray
Cornmeal
1 egg white, beaten (optional)
1 tablespoon water (optional)

☐ Place the yeast and ¹/2 of the white flour in a large mixing bowl with all of the water. Whisk until well combined. Leave this mixture a few minutes until some yeast activity (i.e. bubbles) is visible.

☐ Add the oil and salt, mix well. Gradually add the bran and enough of the remaining flour until the mixture cleans the sides of the bowl.

☐ Turn the dough out onto a lightly floured surface and knead until smooth and elastic, adding small quantities of the reserved flour as necessary or until the dough is no longer sticky.

☐ Return the dough to a lightly oiled bowl, cover and place in a dark, warm, draft-free place to rise until doubled in bulk. This may take 1 to 2 hours depending on heat and humidity (you can create your own heat and humidity to hasten this process by erecting a tent over a sink of hot water in which you have placed the bowl of dough. Replace the hot water as it cools off.)

☐ When the dough has doubled, turn out and punch down. Return to bowl and repeat rising until doubled again. This should happen more quickly than the first time. Lightly grease the cover, particularly during the final rising. An opened out garbage bag works well as a cover and can be used many times. You can omit the second rising if time does not permit. The texture will be a little more coarse and dense.

☐ Divide the dough into equal portions and shape for rolls. The best way to get an even yield is to weigh the dough on a scale. You should expect about 20 large rolls. Place on cookie sheets sprayed with vegetable cooking spray and sprinkled with cornmeal. Allow to rise, covered, until doubled again. Combine egg white and water, brush over rolls if desired. Bake in a preheated 400° F. oven for 20 to 35 minutes. Remove from the oven, turn rolls onto racks to cool.

☐ Makes 20 rolls, 1 roll per serving. (photo page 55)

☐ NOTE: These rolls make excellent containers (when insides scooped out) for soups or beans, they also freeze well.

Per 1 roll serving: Calories 127, Protein 5 g., Fat 2 g., 14% fat (1% saturated fat),
  Carbohydrates 24 g., Dietary fiber 5 g., Cholesterol 0 mg., Sodium 162 mg.,
  Calcium 11 mg., Iron 1 mg.
Exchanges: breads 1¹/2

CRANBERRY NUT BREAD

*2 cups whole wheat pastry flour
1 cup each oat bran and barley flour
1 1/2 cups sugar
3 teaspoons baking powder
1 teaspoon baking soda
1 1/2 cups orange juice

1 cup cooked oatmeal
2 teaspoons grated orange rind
4 tablespoons canola oil
3 egg whites
3 cups cranberries, coarsely chopped
1 cup chopped nuts (lightly roasted)

☐ Preheat oven to 350° F., spray bottoms of two 9x5-inch loaf pans with vegetable cooking spray. In a large bowl, combine first 6 ingredients, mixing well. Set aside. Combine orange juice, oatmeal, orange rind, oil and egg whites; mix well. Fold in cranberries and nuts (reserve a few cranberries and nuts to garnish the top). Stir into dry ingredients then pour into prepared pans. Bake for 55 minutes or until a toothpick inserted into the middle comes out clean. Optional glaze: brush 1 tablespoon melted apple jelly over top of cooled loaves. Makes 2 loaves with 18 slices per loaf.
*Or substitute 1/2 regular whole wheat and 1/2 all-purpose flour. Delicious with Raisin Nut Spread. (photo page 55)

Per 1 slice serving: Calories 125, Protein 2 g., Fat 4 g., 29% fat (2% saturated fat), Carbohydrates 20 g., Dietary fiber 2 g., Cholesterol 0 mg., Sodium 61 mg., Calcium 13 mg., Iron trace.
Exchanges: bread 1/2; fruit 1; fat 1 (Not recommended for diabetics)

Sweet Raisin Nut Spread
1 cup golden raisins
1/2 cup pecans
1 teaspoon vanilla

1 cup very dry Yogurt Cheese, or fat free Philadelphia cream cheese (see page 34)

☐ In the food processor or blender, finely grind the raisins and nuts. Add the vanilla and 1/4 cup of the yogurt cheese; mix well. Transfer to a mixing bowl and fold in remaining yogurt cheese. Refrigerate until ready to use.

☐ Makes 2 cups with 1 tablespoon per serving.

Per 1 tablespoon serving: Calories 37, Protein 1 g., Fat 1 g., 24% fat (3% saturated fat), Carbohydrates 6 g., Dietary fiber trace, Cholesterol 0 mg., Sodium 12 mg., Calcium 32 mg., Iron trace.
Exchanges: fruit 1/2

- Unlike yeasted breads, these breads should be handled as little as possible, just enough to incorporate the ingredients.
- Sift the baking powder and/or soda with the flour to avoid nasty tasting lumps in the final product.

MAIN COURSES

Salmon Pâté
page 38

Stuffed Breast of Chicken with Light Sherry Sauce
page 72

Steamed Fresh Asparagus
page 103

Light and Fluffy Potato Bread with Oat Bran
page 59

Cherry Swirl Cheesecake
page 121

Per serving for complete menu: Calories, 756, Protein 43 g.,
Fat 12 g. (total = 14% saturated = 3%), Carbohydrates 108 g.,
Dietary fiber 8 g., Cholesterol 49 mg., Sodium 712 mg.,
Calcium 381 mg., Iron 6 mg.

This chapter offers a variety of main course dishes. Many are easy and quick and can be whipped up after a hard day at the office. Others included are perfect for entertaining and may involve extra time in preparation. You may find it handy to use the pantry and freezer guide in the back of the book to ensure you have the staples you need.

Photograph: Rich and Creamy Pasta in Parsley Nut Sauce, Stuffed Breast of
Chicken with Light Sherry Sauce, Marinated Flank Steak,
pages 93, 72 and 98

Poultry

CHEF BILL'S RASPBERRY CHICKEN WITH POACHED PEARS

1/4 cup finely diced shallots
2 whole lemons, softened and cut in
   half
1 bunch of parsley, stalks bruised
1/2 teaspoon white pepper
1/4 cup olive oil
1 bay leaf
1 cup raspberry vinegar
6 4-ounce chicken breasts,

skinned, boned and fat removed
3 whole pears
1/2 cup Raspberry Vinegar
1 teaspoon cornstarch or arrowroot
1 tablespoon water
1 pint fresh raspberries
Kale leaves, blanched
Fresh watercress

☐ Combine the shallots, softened lemons, parsley stalks, white pepper, olive oil, bay leaf and 1 cup raspberry vinegar. Pour over the chicken and refrigerate 8 hours or overnight.

☐ Peel pears, cut in half and remove core. Poach the pears in the raspberry vinegar plus enough water to cover until tender, 5 to 15 minutes depending on the ripeness of the pears. Slice vertically from base toward stem, taking care to not cut through stem end.

☐ Remove chicken from marinade, reserving 3 tablespoons marinade. Cook chicken breasts under the broiler or on the grill for 2 to 3 minutes a side or until juices are clear when the chicken is pierced with a fork. Bring reserved marinade to a boil. Dissolve cornstarch in water and add to marinade. Boil 1 minute, stirring constantly.

☐ To serve place the chicken on the kale, pour a little of the thickened marinade over the chicken and garnish with the watercress, fanned poached pear half and fresh raspberries. Excellent accompanied with wild rice salad (page 49).

☐ Makes 6 servings.

☐ NOTE: To make **Raspberry Vinegar**, press 1 pint of fresh or frozen raspberries through a sieve. Add juice to 2 cups wine vinegar.

Per serving: Calories 294, Protein 28 g., Fat 11 g., 34% fat (5% saturated fat),
   Carbohydrates 25 g., Dietary fiber 6 g., Cholesterol 66 mg., Sodium 76 mg.,
   Calcium 60 mg., Iron 2 mg.
Exchanges: lean meat 4; fruit 1 1/2

EASY BREADED POULET DIJON

This breaded chicken recipe is made even easier because only one side is breaded. Most breaded meats go soggy on the bottom when you cut back on the fat, so we eliminated breading on the bottom and you won't even miss it! This is also excellent with seafood fillets such as scrod, sole, orange roughy and tilapia.

3 whole chicken breasts, skinned, boned, defatted and cut in half
1¹/2 teaspoons balsamic vinegar
3 tablespoons Dijon-style mustard
Butter-flavored vegetable spray
1 tablespoon fresh herb of choice such as tarragon, dill or basil (¹/2 teaspoon if using dry)

Freshly ground black pepper to taste
12 tablespoons bread crumbs (made from a couple of slices of whole grain bread)
1 tablespoon freshly grated part skim milk Parmesan cheese

☐ Place chicken breasts in a large flat container with the balsamic vinegar and turn the breasts several times to distribute it evenly.

☐ Spread breasts on both sides with Dijon-style mustard.

☐ Select a clean baking dish to accomodate the breasts in one layer, and spray lightly with butter-flavored vegetable spray.

☐ Combine the herb of choice, pepper, bread crumbs and Parmesan cheese and cover each breast (on top side only).

☐ Arrange breasts in baking dish and bake, uncovered, in preheated 350° F. oven for 25 to 30 minutes. Cooking time will depend on the thickness of the breast. To check for doneness, a small incision in the thickest part of the breast should reveal opaque white flesh; if it is still pink allow more cooking time.

☐ Makes 6 servings.

☐ NOTE: Excellent served with potato wedges (page 102) and a steamed fresh green vegetable in season.

Per serving: Calories 164, Protein 28 g., Fat 4 g., 22% fat (6% saturated fat), Carbohydrates 2 g., Dietary fiber 0.5 g., Cholesterol 73 mg., Sodium 208 mg., Calcium 40 mg., Iron 1 mg.
Exchanges: lean meat 4; fat (-2)

CHICKEN BREASTS STUFFED WITH DUXELLES

1 teaspoon olive oil
1 pound mushrooms, wiped clean, finely chopped
3 large shallots, peeled and finely chopped
1/2 cup chopped parsley

Salt and freshly ground pepper to taste
2 medium zucchini, washed
2 whole chicken breasts, skinned, boned, cut in half
Juice of 1/2 lemon

☐ Preheat oven to 375° F. To make duxelles: Heat the olive oil in a heavy skillet, add the mushrooms and cook until the juices exude. Add the shallots and continue cooking, stirring frequently, until most of the liquid has evaporated. Add the parsley, and season with salt and pepper to taste; cook until heated through.

☐ Slice the zucchini diagonally into 1/8-inch slices and spread evenly on the bottom of a lightly oiled baking dish.

☐ Wipe the chicken breasts with a paper towel and sprinkle with the lemon juice. Place a generous tablespoon of the duxelles in the pocket of each chicken breast half and fold the edges over to make a small package. Secure with a toothpick and place side by side in the baking dish on top of the zucchini.

☐ Bake, loosely covered with foil or waxed paper, in a preheated 375° F. oven for 25 to 30 minutes, depending on the size of the breasts. Great with Lemon Mushroom Sauce.

☐ Makes 6 servings.

Lemon Mushroom Sauce

3 ounces oyster mushrooms, washed
1 teaspoon olive oil
Juice of 1/2 lemon or to taste
2 tablespoons dry Sherry

*1/2 cup concentrated low-sodium chicken stock
2 teaspoons cornstarch

☐ Dissolve cornstarch in 1 tablespoon chicken stock; reserve.

☐ Sauté the mushrooms in the olive oil for 3 to 5 minutes. Add the lemon juice, Sherry and chicken stock and bring to a boil.

☐ Add reserved cornstarch mixture to sauce and boil 1 minute, stirring constantly. Pour over chicken breasts.

☐ *If using canned stock, chill to solidify fat then strain to remove it.

Per serving: Calories 151, Protein 20 g., Fat 3 g., 18% fat (1% saturated fat), Carbohydrates 12 g., Dietary fiber 4 g., Cholesterol 41 mg., Sodium 55 mg., Calcium 38 mg., Iron 2 mg.
Exchanges: lean meat 2; vegetables 2

LIGHTLY BREADED (OAT BRAN) CHICKEN BREASTS

1 teaspoon frozen tarragon (1½ teaspoons fresh or ½ teaspoon dry)
1 teaspoon lemon and herb seasoning
1 teaspoon Raspberry Vinegar (page 67)

2 teaspoons olive oil
6 3-ounce chicken breasts, skinned, boned, fat removed
1 tablespoon freshly grated part skim milk Parmesan cheese
2 tablespoons oat bran

☐ Preheat oven to 350° F.

☐ Combine the tarragon, lemon and herb seasonings, raspberry vinegar and olive oil in a dish large enough to hold all the breasts without overlapping. Mix well and coat the breasts and marinate for 10 to 20 minutes.

☐ Combine the cheese and oat bran in another container or a paper bag. Coat each chicken breast with the oat bran-cheese mixture, if using a paper bag, put them in 1 at a time and shake them to coat. Layer the breasts in a single layer in a baking pan and bake in a preheated oven for 20-30 minutes. Turn oven on to broil and place the chicken breasts about 4 inches from the broiler for an additional 3 minutes each side to crisp them. Excellent served with Lemon Mushroom Sauce (page 69) accompanied by Easy Rice Pilaf (page 107) and a steamed green vegetable in season.

☐ Makes 6 servings.

Per serving: Calories 118, Protein 20 g., Fat 3 g., 23% fat (5% saturated fat), Cholesterol 50 mg., Carbohydrates 1 g., Dietary fiber trace, Sodium 70 mg., Calcium 21 mg., Iron 0.7 mg.
Exchanges: lean meat 3; fat (-1)

LEMONY GRILLED CHICKEN BREASTS

2 cups plain nonfat yogurt
¼ cup lemon juice
2 tablespoons Worcestershire sauce
1 teaspoon fresh ground black pepper

1 teaspoon freshly grated ginger
1 teaspoon fruity olive oil
3 whole chicken breasts, skinned, boned and all visible fat removed
Hungarian paprika

☐ Combine first 6 ingredients, marinate and cook the chicken according to marinade directions (page 96). Sprinkle with paprika toward the end of the cooking time.

☐ Makes 6 servings.

Per serving: Calories 151, Protein 24 g., Fat 2 g., 12% fat (3% saturated fat), Carbohydrates 8 g., Dietary fiber 0 g., Cholesterol 51 mg., Sodium 163 mg., Calcium 168 mg., Iron 1 mg.
Exchanges: lean meat 3; skim milk ½; fat (-1)

BAKED CHICKEN BREASTS TO RIVAL THE COLONEL'S

6 split chicken breasts, skinned,
  boned and all visible fat removed
1 teaspoon Mrs. Dash lemon and
  herb seasoning
1/2 teaspoon minced garlic (1 clove)
2 teaspoons light soy sauce

Dash hot pepper sauce
1 egg white
2 tablespoons freshly grated part
  skim milk Parmesan cheese
2 whole grain bread slices
Spray olive oil

☐ Preheat oven to 400° F.

☐ Sprinkle the chicken breasts with Mrs. Dash and set aside. Combine the garlic, soy sauce, hot sauce, and egg white; whisk with fork. Grate the Parmesan, (you can do this very quickly if you cut it up into cubes and put it in your food processor for a minute or so). Add the bread and pulse the food processor a couple more times. If you do not have a food processor, grate the cheese manually and crumble the bread by rubbing it between your fingers. Place bread mixture on a flat dish or plate.

☐ Spray a broiler pan with a vegetable cooking spray, dip the chicken into the egg white mixture, then into the bread crumbs, 1 piece at a time, place on broiler pan. Spray with the olive oil and bake for 10 minutes; turn and return to the oven for a further 5 minutes. Serve with Lemon Mushroom Sauce (page 69), steamed vegetables in season and crusty whole wheat braids (page 61).

☐ Makes 6 servings.

Per serving: Calories 140, Protein 22 g., Fat 3 g., 19% fat (4% saturated fat),
  Carbohydrates 5 g., Dietary fiber 0 mg., Cholesterol 50 mg., Sodium 157 mg.,
  Calcium 42 mg., Iron 1 mg.
Exchanges: lean meat 3; fat (-1); bread 1/2

BARBECUED CHICKEN

1/2 cup lemon juice
Zest of 1 lemon
1 tablespoon olive oil
3 tablespoons fresh mint
3 cloves of garlic, finely chopped

3/4 cup dry Sherry
2 tablespoons white wine
  Worcestershire sauce
1 whole chicken, skinned, fat
  removed, cut up

☐ Combine first 7 ingredients in a saucepan, bring to a boil, cool. Marinate and cook chicken according to general directions (page 96).

☐ Makes 6 servings.

Per serving: Calories 204, Protein 24 g., Fat 6 g., 26% fat (6% saturated fat),
  *Carbohydrates 6 g., Dietary fiber 0 g., Cholesterol 77 mg., Sodium 136 mg.,
  Calcium 26 mg., Iron 1 mg.
Exchanges: lean meat 3; *(fruit 1/2, may be discarded with marinade)

STUFFED BREAST OF CHICKEN WITH LIGHT SHERRY SAUCE

2/3 cup finely chopped shallots
2 teaspoons olive oil
2 cloves of garlic, shoot removed
  and finely chopped
1/3 cup diced red pepper
1/3 cup diced celery
3/4 pound mushrooms, wiped clean
  and finely chopped
3/4 cup dry Sherry
1/3 cup fresh basil
1/2 cup fresh parsley, finely chopped
1 cup diced tomato
1 teaspoon barley miso or 1
  tablespoon reduced-sodium soy
  sauce
2 sun-dried tomatoes, finely chopped
2/3 cup oat bran

4 whole chicken breasts, skinned,
  boned, fat removed, cut in half
Freshly ground black pepper
  (optional)
1 cup julienne red pepper
2 cups julienne carrots
1/2 cup chopped scallions
3/4 cup chicken stock (low sodium)
2 tablespoons dry Sherry
1 to 2 teaspoons cornstarch or
  arrowroot
2 teaspoons water
1/2 to 1 teaspoon barley miso or 1
  tablespoon reduced-sodium soy
  sauce
1/4 teaspoon salt (optional)

☐ Preheat oven to 325° F.

☐ In a large heavy-gauge sauté pan, over moderate heat, sauté the shallots in the olive oil 2 to 3 minutes. Add the garlic and cook an additional 2 to 3 minutes or until translucent. Add the diced red pepper, celery and mushrooms and cook until the mushrooms wilt and exude their juices. Add the Sherry, turn up the heat and evaporate off 1/4th the liquid. Add the basil, parsley, tomatoes, miso, sun-dried tomatoes and oat bran. Stir well to combine, then taste for seasonings, adjusting as desired.

☐ Slice each breast half horizontally taking care to not cut all the way through and open it out like the center fold of a magazine. Season with pepper if desired and mound 1/8 of the stuffing on one side. Fold the other side over to partially cover the stuffing.

☐ Place the red peppers, carrots and scallions in a lightly oiled baking pan. Arrange the chicken breasts on top and pour in enough of the chicken stock to cover the bottom of the pan, reserving the remainder for the sauce. Cover with foil. Bake in preheated 325° F. oven for 12 minutes. Turn chicken, scooping up vegetable mixture to top, cook an additional 10 to 15 minutes. Avoid overcooking.

☐ Remove the chicken breasts to a warm platter and cover. Transfer juices in the pan and remaining chicken stock to a saucepan, add the dry Sherry and bring to a boil. Dissolve cornstarch in water and add to sauce. Boil 1 minute. (If using arrowroot do not boil after the sauce thickens as it will become thin again). Stir in miso and salt. Pour the sauce over the chicken breasts and serve at once. Great with steamed fresh vegetables in season and crusty French bread. Makes 8 servings. (photo page 65)

Per serving: Calories 205, Protein 21 g., Fat 3 g., 13% fat (2% saturated fat),
  Carbohydrates 17 g., Dietary fiber 4 g., Cholesterol 41 mg., Sodium 125 mg.,
  Calcium 64 mg., Iron 2 mg.
Exchanges: lean meat 2; vegetables 2; bread 1/2

QUICK 'N EASY LIGHTLY CURRIED CHICKEN

The condiments dress up this dish and add an exciting freshness. Serve them separately in individual containers.

1 tablespoon canola oil
2 medium onions, chopped
3 cloves of garlic, shoot removed
  and finely chopped
1 whole chicken breast, skinned,
  boned and all visible fat removed
1 to 2 teaspoons Madras curry
  powder or to taste

1 package your favorite low sodium
  vegetable soup mix
1/2 cup dry Sherry
Juice of 1 lemon
1/4 cup raisins

☐ Heat oil over medium heat, add the onions and sauté for 10 minutes or until transparent. Do not allow to brown as this will make them bitter. Add the garlic and continue to cook 5 to 10 minutes.

☐ Cut the chicken into bite-sized pieces, add to the onions and garlic, stirring to cook evenly. When the chicken is opaque, add the curry powder, cook 5 minutes, then add the soup mix, dry Sherry, lemon juice and raisins. Stir well until the liquid boils, add water if too thick, partially cover and simmer 20 minutes.

☐ Best served over rice accompanied with steamed fresh vegetables in season.

☐ Makes 4 servings.

Condiments:

2 bunches scallions, finely chopped
2 cups diced fresh pineapple
1 cup diced fresh tomatoes

1/2 cup fresh coriander leaf,
  coarsely chopped

Per serving: Calories 304, Protein 16 g., Fat 6 g., 18% fat (2% saturated fat),
  Carbohydrates 36 g., Dietary fiber 4 g., Cholesterol 32 mg., Sodium 332 mg.,
  Calcium 64 mg., Iron 1.6 mg.
Exchanges: lean meat 1; vegetable 4; fruit 1

QUICK AND HEARTY BURRITOS WITH ALL THE TRIMMINGS

2 whole chicken breasts, skinned,
  boned and all visible fat removed
2 tablespoons freshly squeezed lime
  juice
1 tablespoon tamari or low-sodium
  soy sauce
1/2 teaspoon sugar (or 2 teaspoons
  apple jelly)
1 clove of garlic, crushed
1 recipe Refried Beans (page 106)
1   (14-ounce) can stewed tomatoes,
  no-salt added
2 tablespoons tomato paste
8 large burrito wraps
1/2 cup freshly grated part skim
  milk Parmesan cheese (optional)

☐ Prepare the chicken breast and place in a shallow dish; set aside.

☐ Combine the following 4 ingredients and pour over the chicken and allow to marinate for at least 1/2 hour or up to 4 hours.

☐ Prepare refried beans.

☐ Combine stewed tomatoes and tomato paste and purée in a food processor or blender.

☐ Remove chicken from marinade and broil for 2 to 3 minutes per side or until just cooked through; cut into thin strips (1/4 inch).

☐ Fill the burritos with the refried beans, sprinkle with the thin strips of chicken and roll up. Place in a lightly oiled baking dish. Pour tomato sauce over and sprinkle with Parmesan cheese if desired.

☐ Bake in a preheated 375° F. oven for 30 minutes or until bubbly. Tent with foil if the cheese browns too quickly. Serve with Mexican garnishes such as Guacamole (page 39), salsa (you can buy this in a jar) and yogurt sour cream (page 34).

☐ Makes 8 servings.

Per serving: Calories 463, Protein 28 g., Fat 10 g., 19% fat (* saturated fat),
  Carbohydrates 65 g., Dietary fiber 13 g., Cholesterol 32 mg., Sodium 1014 mg.,
  Calcium 170 mg., Iron 4 mg. *Data not available at this time.
Exchanges: lean meat 2; bread 4; vegetable 1; fat 1

QUICK CAJUN CHICKEN OVER RICE

2 medium onions, peeled, chopped
1 tablespoon olive oil
3 cloves of garlic, shoot removed
  and minced
2 whole chicken breasts, skinned,
  boned and all visible fat removed
  and cut into bite-sized pieces

1 to 1½ teaspoons Cajun seasoning
  or to taste
2 ripe tomatoes, diced
¾ cup dry Sherry
8 cups cooked brown rice

☐ In a heavy saucepan, sauté the onions in the olive oil until transparent. Add the garlic and sauté an additional 5 minutes.

☐ Add the chicken and Cajun seasoning. Cook over medium-high heat until the chicken is opaque, stirring constantly. Add the tomatoes and Sherry and simmer, covered, for 20 minutes. Serve over rice accompanied by steamed fresh broccoli flowerettes.

☐ Makes 8 servings.

Per serving: Calories 334, Protein 14 g., Fat 3 g., 8% fat (1% saturated fat),
  Carbohydrates 55 g., Dietary fiber 5 g., Cholesterol 20 mg., Sodium 59 mg.,
  Calcium 16 mg., Iron 1.5 mg.
Exchanges: lean meat 1; vegetable 1; bread 3

HONEY-GLAZED SOY CHICKEN

Enough for a whole chicken, 3 whole breasts cut in half or a comparable amount of firm flesh fish such as swordfish, halibut, marlin, tuna or lean pork.

1 tablespoon olive oil
¼ cup red wine vinegar
2 teaspoons low-sodium soy sauce
2 teaspoons Dijon-style mustard
Freshly ground black pepper to
  taste

1 tablespoon brown sugar
1 whole chicken, skinned, fat
  removed, cut into 6 serving
  portions
2 tablespoons honey

☐ Combine first 6 ingredients in a saucepan, bring to a boil, cool. Marinate chicken and cook according to general directions (page 96). When almost cooked, combine the honey with the remaining marinade, and baste the meat until golden brown and fully cooked.

☐ Makes 6 servings.

Per serving: Calories 184, Protein 24 g., Fat 6 g., 29% fat (6% saturated fat),
  *Carbohydrates 9 g., Dietary fiber 0 g., Cholesterol 77 mg., Sodium 174 mg.,
  Calcium 19 mg., Iron 1 mg.
Exchanges: lean meat 3; *(fruit ½, may be discarded with marinade)

SPICY TURKEY CHILI

1 pound lean ground turkey
1 onion, chopped
1 1³/₄-ounce package chili
   seasonings (Carroll Shelby's)
1 pound frozen whole kernel corn
2 (14-ounce) cans red kidney beans

2 (14¹/₂-ounce) cans stewed
   tomatoes (no salt added)
2 tablespoons tomato paste
1 cup tomato purée
¹/₂ teaspoon salt (optional)
Dash of hot sauce

☐ In a large heavy saucepan, sauté the turkey on low heat, stirring constantly until it gives off moisture. Add the onion and chili seasonings and increase heat, continue to sauté until slightly brown. Add the remaining ingredients, bring to a boil, reduce heat. Simmer for 30 to 40 minutes. Excellent over baked potatoes.

☐ Makes 8 servings.

Per Serving: Calories 283, Protein 20 g., Fat 6 g., 19% fat (* saturated fat),
   Carbohydrates 40 g., Dietary fiber 11 g., Cholesterol 37 mg., Sodium 569 mg.,
   Calcium 54 mg., Iron 2.6 mg. *Data not available at this time.
Exchanges: lean meat 2; bread 2; vegetable 2

RICE AND TURKEY STIR-FRY

2 cups uncooked brown rice, cooked
1 onion, diced
1 tablespoon olive oil
3 cloves of garlic
1 pound turkey breast, cut into thin
   strips
¹/₂ pound mushrooms
1 medium zucchini, sliced
   diagonally

¹/₄ cup lemon juice, freshly squeezed
¹/₄ cup tamari or low sodium soy
   sauce
2 tablespoons fresh coriander leaf,
   coarsely chopped
¹/₄ cup fresh parsley, finely chopped
1 tablespoon sesame seeds

☐ Sauté onion in olive oil over medium heat until soft, (about 10 minutes), add the garlic and continue to cook an additional 5 minutes. Add turkey tossing to cook on all sides. Add the mushrooms and cook for 5 minutes. Increase heat, add zucchini, cook 3 to 4 minutes. Toss ingredients to combine well, add the lemon juice and tamari. Add the reserved rice and cook until heated through, stirring frequently. Stir in the coriander leaf and parsley. Garnish with sesame seeds and serve at once.

☐ Makes 8 servings.

☐ NOTE: Left over cooked turkey works well if added near the end of cooking time.

Per serving: Calories 280, Protein 19 g., Fat 4 g., 13% fat (2% saturated fat),
   Carbohydrates 42 g., Dietary fiber 5 g., Cholesterol 36 mg., Sodium 331 mg.,
   Calcium 31 mg., Iron 2 mg.
Exchanges: meat 1; bread 2¹/₂; vegetables 1

SUCCULENT GRILLED OR BROILED TURKEY BURGERS

1¹/₂ pounds ground lean turkey
1 egg white
¹/₄ cup chopped scallions
2 cloves of garlic, shoot removed, mashed
2 tablespoons freshly ground part skim milk Parmesan cheese

1 teaspoon lemon and herb seasoning
2 tablespoons Worcestershire sauce
2 slices oat bran bread, ground to fine bread crumbs in your food processor
¹/₂ teaspoon olive oil

☐ In a large mixing bowl, combine all the ingredients except the olive oil. Knead to incorporate all the ingredients then shape into 6 large patties.

☐ Lightly oil a broiler pan and or grill with the olive oil, then arrange the patties on the pan without overlapping, sprinkle with additional lemon and herb seasoning. Broil for 5 minutes 4 inches from a preheated broiler. Turn the patties and cook an additional 3 to 4 minutes or until the meat springs back when depressed. Serve garnished with lettuce and fresh tomato slices. These are delicious served in crusty oat bran rolls (page 63) which have been spread with your favorite mustard.

☐ Makes 6 large burgers.

Per serving: Calories 210, Protein 26 g., Fat 10 g., 43% fat (* saturated fat),
  Carbohydrates 7 g., Dietary fiber 1 g., Cholesterol 74 mg., Sodium 88 mg.,
  Calcium 43 mg., Iron .8 mg. *Data not available at this time.
Exchanges: lean meat 3¹/₂; bread ¹/₂

Quick Hearty Red Sauce for Meatballs

1 medium shallot, finely chopped
1 tablespoon Greek dressing
1¹/₂ cups tomato purée
¹/₂ cup dry red wine
¹/₂ cup chicken stock

1 tablespoon tomato paste
2 tablespoons tomato ketchup
1 to 2 dashes hot sauce
1 recipe Turkey Burger Mixture shaped into meatballs*

☐ In a heavy saucepan, sauté shallots in the dressing for 5 minutes or until wilted. Add next 7 ingredients. Bring to a boil, reduce heat. Cover, simmer, stirring occasionally, for 30 minutes.

☐ Shape Turkey Burger mixture into 48 meatballs, add to sauce. Simmer for 20 minutes. *(Add ¹/₂ teaspoon Italian seasoning before shaping into balls if desired.)

☐ Makes 8 servings.

☐ NOTE: Serve as a pasta sauce, over rice, as a filling for submarine sandwiches, or as an hors d'oeuvre.

Per sauce serving: Calories 205, Protein 21 g., Fat 9 g., 40% fat (* saturated fat),
  Carbohydrates 12 g., Dietary fiber 1 g., Cholesterol 56 mg., Sodium 141 mg.,
  Calcium 42 mg., Iron 1.6 mg. *Data not available at this time.

Seafood

We have intentionally selected seafood which is high in heart healthy Omega-3 fatty acids. Therefore in these recipes the higher percent fat is beneficial.

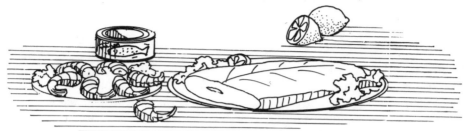

BAKED FISH FILLETS IN PARCHMENT

Inspired by a memorable dinner in Nashville! We like to use salmon for this recipe, although Cape bluefish, swordfish or black cod would also be delicious. The parchment seals in the flavors and keeps the fish moist.

1¹/₂ pounds fish fillets
1 tablespoon prepared mustard
2 to 3 teaspoons green peppercorns, crushed or to taste
1 medium sweet, mild onion, thinly sliced (optional)
¹/₂ cup scallions, finely chopped
2 tablespoons lemon thyme or fresh herb of choice, finely chopped

18 slices sun-dried tomatoes (about 1¹/₂ ounces) or 6 pieces oil-cured, cut julienne
¹/₄ cup dry vermouth
Parchment paper, cut into 6 approximately 12-inch squares, enough to wrap the fish in securely.

☐ Preheat oven to 450° F.

☐ Cut the fish into 6 serving-size pieces and place them on the parchment. Spread each piece lightly with the mustard. Sprinkle with the crushed green peppercorns then arrange the onion, scallions and herb on top. Arrange 3 sun-dried tomato slices on the very top, drizzle each fillet with 2 teaspoons of vermouth and wrap up the package. Take care to fold the edges over several times for a tight seal. Place in the middle of the preheated oven for 15 to 20 minutes depending on the thickness of the fish. You need to allow 10 minutes per inch of thickness plus 10 minutes more for this dish. Serve immediately in their wrapping. Delicious accompanied with steamed fresh vegetable in season and a baked potato with nonfat yogurt sour cream (page 34).

☐ Makes 6 servings.

Per serving: Calories 170, Protein 24 g., Fat 5 g., 26% fat (5% saturated fat), Carbohydrates 4 g., Dietary fiber 1 g., Cholesterol 67 mg., Sodium 104 mg., Calcium 30 mg., Iron 1 mg.
Exchanges: lean meat 3; vegetable 1; fat (-1)

EASY CAJUN CAPE BLUEFISH WITH OAT BRAN

Alternative fish: Wolffish or sea trout

2 pounds Cape bluefish fillets
Juice of 1 lemon
1 teaspoon Cajun spices

1 tablespoon oat bran
2 tablespoons olive oil

☐ Wipe fish with paper towel, place on a platter skin side down. Pour the lemon juice over the fish and allow to stand 5 minutes. Sprinkle evenly with the Cajun spices, then the oat bran, pressing it into the fish. Do this on the top side only.

☐ Heat the olive oil in a sauté pan to sizzling hot, carefully place the fish into the pan, skin side down, and cook over moderately high heat for 5 minutes. Place the sauté pan under a preheated broiler for 3 to 5 minutes. Cooking time will depend on the thickness of the fish and the rule of thumb is to allow 10 minutes for every inch of thickness at the thickest part of the fish. Keep cooked fish loosely covered in a 250° F. oven while you cook the remaining pieces.

☐ Makes 8 servings.

Per serving: Calories 175, Protein 23 g., Fat 8 g., 41% fat (8% saturated fat),
Carbohydrates 1 g., Dietary fiber trace, Cholesterol 67 mg., Sodium 100 mg.,
Calcium 9 mg., Iron 0.5 mg.
Exchanges: lean meat 3

BROILED MARINATED CAPE BLUEFISH

2¹/₂ pounds Cape bluefish
3 tablespoons Raspberry Vinegar
(page 67)
Juice and zest from 1 lemon
1 tablespoon extra virgin olive oil
1 shallot, finely chopped

1 tablespoon fresh dill, finely
chopped
One bunch of fresh parsley
2 tablespoons fresh garlic tops,
finely chopped
Freshly ground black pepper

☐ Wipe the fish clean with a paper towel. Combine the remaining ingredients, pour over the fish in a ziplock plastic bag. Marinate for at least 1 hour but no longer than 4 hours or it will become tough, turning the bag from time to time.

☐ Preheat the grill or broiler. Remove the fish from the marinade. Cook the fish 2 inches from the broiler for 5 minutes, turn and cook 5 minutes on the other side, basting with the liquid from the marinade. Cooking time will vary depending on the thickness of the fish. Serve garnished with 6 lemon slices and 6 sprigs of fresh dill.

☐ Makes 6 servings.

Per serving: Calories 250, Protein 38 g., Fat 10 g., 36% fat (1% saturated fat),
Carbohydrates 2 g., Dietary fiber trace, Cholesterol 111 mg., Sodium 114 mg.,
Calcium 21 mg., Iron 1 mg.
Exchanges: lean meat 5; fat (-1)

BROILED CAPE BLUEFISH WITH DIJON MUSTARD

3 pounds Cape bluefish
2 large cloves of garlic, finely
   minced
2 teaspoons prepared Dijon-style
   mustard
1/4 cup finely chopped fresh dill or
   1 tablespoon dried dill

Freshly ground black pepper to
   taste
1 teaspoon olive oil
Slices of lemon and sprigs of
   watercress for garnish

☐ (Begin 1 hour before cooking.) Arrange fillets on a large platter skin side down. Sprinkle with garlic, then spread with mustard and finally sprinkle with the fresh dill and pepper. Allow to stand 1 hour before cooking.

☐ Arrange fillets on a lightly oiled broiler pan and cook under a preheated broiler for 5 to 10 minutes depending on the thickness of the fish. The best guide to cooking fish is to allow 10 minutes per inch of thickness from the thickest part of the fish. Broil 6 to 8 inches from the heating element. Serve garnished with a lemon slice and fresh watercress with steamed new potatoes and a fresh green vegetable in season.

☐ Makes 8 servings.

Per serving: Calories 219, Protein 34 g., Fat 8 g., 33% fat (7% saturated fat),
   Carbohydrates 1 g., , Dietary fiber trace, Cholesterol 100 mg., Sodium 119 mg.,
   Calcium 23 mg., Iron 1 mg.
Exchanges: lean meat 5; fat (-1)

BABY MACKEREL FILLETS WITH OAT BRAN COATING

6 3 to 4-ounce fresh mackerel
   fillets
Juice of 1/2 lemon

Freshly ground pepper to taste
1 tablespoon olive oil
1/2 cup oat bran

☐ Pat the fillets dry with paper towel. Sprinkle with lemon juice and pepper.

☐ Preheat sauté pan with 1 teaspoon olive oil over medium high heat.

☐ Sprinkle oat bran over fish and pat into crevices, turning to coat both sides. Sauté skin side down 2 minutes, turn and cook an additional 3 minutes or until cooked through, adding more oil if necessary. Serve with a garnish of fresh lemon and a sprig of watercress. Excellent accompanied by a seasonal salad and steamed brown rice tossed with fresh basil.

☐ Makes 6 servings.

Per serving: Calories 272, Protein 22 g., Fat 18 g., 60% fat (13% saturated fat),
   Carbohydrates 5 g., Dietary fiber 1 g., Cholesterol 64 mg., Sodium 71 mg.,
   Calcium 14 mg., Iron 1.4 mg.
Exchanges: lean meat 3; bread 1/2; fat 2

STEAMED BLACK COD STEAKS

You can substitute halibut steaks or for a dramatic presentation try a whole snapper, walleye, black bass or flounder.

1 tablespoon fresh ginger, grated
1 large clove of garlic, shoot
  removed, minced
2 8-ounce black cod steaks, cut
  in half

1/2 cup finely julienne carrots
2 tablespoons thinly sliced green
  onion

☐ Bring 2 to 3 inches of water to boil in fish steamer.

☐ Combine the ginger and garlic and spread over the fish. Place fish in the steamer, 2 inches above the water. Sprinkle with carrots and onions, cover tightly. Steam for 10 minutes per inch measured at the thickest part of the fish or until barely opaque.

☐ Makes 4 servings.

> **Per serving:** Calories 235, Protein 16 g., Fat 17 g., 65% fat (14% saturated fat), Carbohydrates 3 g., Dietary fiber 1 g., Cholesterol 56 mg., Sodium 76 mg., Calcium 13 mg., Iron 1.7 mg.
> **Exchanges:** meat 2; vegetables 1/2; fat 2

EASY BROILED SCROD WITH AN ORIENTAL FLAIR

1 tablespoon sesame oil
6 6-ounce pieces scrod
1 teaspoon freshly grated ginger

2 cloves of garlic, shoot removed
  and minced

☐ Lightly grease the broiler pan with a little of the sesame oil, then arrange the scrod on the pan without overlapping.

☐ Combine the ginger, garlic and remaining sesame oil to make a sauce and brush liberally over the scrod.

☐ Broil under a preheated broiler, 4 inches from the element for 10 minutes per inch of thickness measured from the thickest part of the scrod. Baste frequently with remaining sauce until all used up.

☐ Makes 6 servings.

☐ NOTE: We suggest serving with gazpacho salad (page 48), steamed pea pods and crusty French bread.

> **Per serving:** Calories 200, Protein 39 g., Fat 4 g., 18% fat (3% saturated fat), Carbohydrates 1 g., Dietary fiber trace, Cholesterol 94 mg., Sodium 132 mg., Calcium 26 mg., Iron 0.9 mg.
> **Exchanges:** lean meat 51/2; fat (-2)

BAKED FISH WITH WALNUTS AND CORIANDER

1 1/2 cups coriander leaves
1/2 cup walnut pieces, lightly roasted
Juice of 1/2 lemon
3 cloves of garlic, flattened and
  shoot removed
1 medium jalapeño pepper, seeded
  and coarsely chopped

Salt to taste (optional)
1 teaspoon olive oil
6 3-ounce pieces fish (halibut,
  swordfish, tuna or rock cod)
Toasted walnut pieces for garnish

☐ Preheat oven to 400° F.

☐ Combine the first 4 ingredients in a food processor or blender and pulse to a coarse paste, mix in salt if desired.

☐ Lightly lubricate a shallow baking pan (just large enough to hold the fish without overlapping) with the olive oil. Arrange fish in the pan, spread evenly with all the coriander mixture, and bake in a preheated 400° F. oven until fish is opaque. Allow an extra 10 minutes before applying the 10 minutes per inch rule. Serve with steamed new potatoes and green vegetables, and garnish with the reserved toasted walnut pieces. This fish is particularly good with nutty brown rice and green beans with roasted almonds.

☐ Makes 6 servings.

Per Serving: Calories 200, Protein 24 g., Fat 10 g., 45% fat (5% saturated fat),
  Carbohydrates 3 g., Dietary fiber 1 g., Cholesterol 35 mg., Sodium 82 mg.,
  Calcium 69 mg., Iron 1 mg.
Exchanges: lean meat 3 1/2

BROILED NORWEGIAN SALMON

2 8-ounce salmon fillets, halved
1/2 teaspoon extra virgin olive oil
Hungarian paprika

Freshly ground black pepper
4 lemon wedges

☐ Brush fish with oil, sprinkle with paprika and pepper.

☐ Broil 10 minutes per inch, no need to turn. Squeeze lemon over the fish and serve immediately.

☐ Makes 4 servings.

Per Serving: Calories 200, Protein 24 g., Fat 10 g., 45% fat (8% saturated fat),
  Carbohydrates 2 g., Dietary fiber trace, Cholesterol 71 mg., Sodium 54 mg.,
  Calcium 16 mg., Iron 0.8 mg.
Exchanges: lean meat 3 1/2

BREADED BAKED ORANGE ROUGHY

1/3 cup nonfat plain yogurt
1 clove of garlic, shoot removed
  and minced
1 tablespoon lemon juice, freshly
  squeezed
1 teaspoon lemon zest, finely
  chopped

2 pounds Orange Roughy or other
  mild Whitefish
4 slices oat bran bread, shredded to
  make crumbs
2 tablespoons freshly grated part
  skim milk Parmesan cheese
2 teaspoons olive oil

☐ Preheat oven to 400 F.

☐ Combine the yogurt, garlic, lemon juice and lemon zest. Pour over fish, turning the fish to coat all sides and allow to marinate for 1 to 3 hours in refrigerator.

☐ Combine the bread crumbs, grated Parmesan cheese and olive oil.

☐ Spread the bread crumb mixture out over a large platter and dip each piece of fish into the crumbs to coat both sides.

☐ Place the fish on a lightly oiled broiler pan and bake for 10 minutes. Place the fish about 4 to 5 inches from the heating element and broil 2 to 3 minutes. Turn and broil for 1 minute. Serve with Cucumber Dill Sauce.

☐ Makes 6 servings.

Cucumber Dill Sauce

1/2 cup nonfat plain yogurt
1/2 cup seeded, peeled and finely
  chopped cucumber
1/2 teaspoon Dijon mustard

1 teaspoon fresh or frozen dill
  (1/4 teaspoon dry)
1/2 teaspoon salt (optional)

☐ Combine all ingredients and stir well. Serve in a separate bowl or sauce boat.

☐ Makes 6 servings.

Per Serving: Calories 293, Protein 27 g., Fat 14 g., 43% fat (2% saturated fat),
  Carbohydrates 14 g., Dietary fiber 1 g., Cholesterol 32 mg., Sodium 333 mg.,
  Calcium 114 mg., Iron 1.1 mg.
Exchanges: lean meat 3 1/2; bread 1; fat 1/2

LIGHT AND LEMONY BROILED SCALLOPS

Great with wild rice and stir-fry vegetables.

1¹/₂ pounds sea scallops	Juice and zest of 1 lemon
3 tablespoons dry Sherry	1 teaspoon cornstarch
3 tablespoons teriyaki sauce	1 tablespoon water

☐ Combine the scallops and next 3 ingredients in a shallow dish. Marinate at least 2 hours or overnight in the refrigerator.

☐ Remove the scallops from the marinade (reserve the marinade), and broil 3 inches from heat for 3 minutes. Keep warm while you prepare the sauce.

☐ Dissolve cornstarch in water. Bring the reserved marinade to a boil and add the cornstarch. Return to a boil and boil for 1 minute. Pour over the scallops and serve over rice or serve as an appetizer with the sauce on the side for "dipping."

☐ Makes 6 servings or 12 appetizer servings.

Per Serving: Calories 125, Protein 20 g., Fat 1 g., 7% fat (1% saturated fat), Carbohydrates 8 g., Dietary fiber 0 g., Cholesterol 38 mg., Sodium 527 mg., Calcium 40 mg., Iron 0.6 mg.
Exchanges: lean meat 3; fat (-2); fruit ¹/₂

STIR-FRY SESAME SHRIMP

One of the many excellent recipes shared with us by Mike and Frank at Monahan's Seafood Market.

³/₄ pound medium shrimp (18 to 24)	¹/₄ cup thinly diagonally sliced
1 tablespoon canola oil	green onions
1 tablespoon light soy sauce	1 tablespoon grated fresh ginger
1 tablespoon sesame seeds	

☐ Peel and devein the shrimp.

☐ In a frying pan or wok, heat the oil until sizzling hot, add soy sauce, sesame seeds and shrimp. Stir-fry 2 to 3 minutes over high heat. Add the onion and ginger, stir-fry 1 minute. Serve immediately. Great over rice accompanied by steamed green beans with slivered almonds.

☐ Makes 6 servings.

Per Serving: Calories 91, Protein 12 g., Fat 4 g., 40% fat (5% saturated fat), Carbohydrates 1 g., Dietary fiber 1 g., Cholesterol 86 mg., Sodium 185 mg., Calcium 4 mg., Iron 1.6 mg.
Exchanges: lean meat 2

SHRIMP IN TARRAGON SAUCE WITH MUSHROOMS

1/2 cup dry Sherry

2 teaspoons finely chopped fresh
tarragon (or 1 teaspoon dry)

3 cloves of garlic, peeled, shoots
removed and mashed

10 ounces fresh or frozen medium
raw shrimp, peeled and deveined
and cut in half lengthwise

1 1/2 cups uncooked long grain
brown rice cooked to package
directions or 16 ounces of your
favorite pasta

2 bunches scallions, washed and
chopped finely

2 teaspoons olive oil

1 red pepper, washed, cored and
julienned

3 large fresh oyster mushrooms,
wiped clean and sliced

1/2 pound fresh mushrooms, wiped
clean and thinly sliced

6 ounces low-fat cheese, such as
feta, cubed

1/2 cup fresh parsley, washed and
finely chopped

1/2 cup freshly grated part skim
milk Parmesan cheese

☐ Combine the Sherry, tarragon and garlic. Add the shrimp and marinate overnight in the refrigerator or for 1 hour at room temperature.

☐ Cook the rice or heat the water for the pasta.

☐ Sauté the scallions in the olive oil over low heat until tender. Add the red pepper and mushrooms and sauté for 5 minutes or until the mushrooms release their juices.

☐ Push the vegetables to the side of the pan and add the shrimp, reserving the marinade. In a separate saucepan bring the reserved marinade to a boil then simmer 2 to 3 minutes. Combine with the feta cheese in a food processor or blender and process until smooth.

☐ Toss the cooked rice or pasta with the cheese mixture, then add the shrimp and mushrooms. Garnish with fresh parsley and serve hot with grated Parmesan cheese.

☐ Makes 6 servings.

Per Serving: Calories 401, Protein 22 g., Fat 11 g., 25% fat (13% saturated fat),
Carbohydrates 48 g., Dietary fiber 7 g., Cholesterol 102 mg., Sodium 503 mg.,
Calcium 277 mg., Iron 3.8 mg.
Exchanges: lean meat 1; bread 2 1/2; skim milk 1/2; fat 1; vegetables 1

Pasta

Ah pasta! Did you know that we should actually credit the Chinese with the discovery of pasta rather than the Italians? However, the Italians deserve an honorable mention for expanding our horizons. Whatever the case, pasta is universally popular and easy to fix. In this section you will find a wealth of exciting and original recipes to satisfy and delight the most critical of pasta lovers. As with all the main course recipes, the pasta recipe gives you a high percentage of complex carbohydrates, low fat and moderate protein.

HERBED ORZO

Great as a side dish to accompany grilled seafood or chicken.

1 pound rice shaped pasta (orzo)
1/2 teaspoon leaf marjoram
  (2 teaspoons if available fresh)
3 tablespoons fresh parsley, finely
  chopped
1 tablespoon fresh rosemary (or
  other fresh herb)
1 cup diced red or yellow bell
  pepper

1/4 cup green onion tops, finely
  chopped
1/2 teaspoon green peppercorns,
  ground
1 teaspoon finely chopped lemon
  zest
1/2 teaspoon salt
1/8 teaspoon freshly grated nutmeg
1 tablespoon* olive oil

☐ Cook pasta until *al dente*; drain and toss with remaining ingredients. Serve warm or at room temperature.

☐ Makes 8 cups.

Variation: Add 1 tablespoon finely chopped sun-dried tomatoes, use the *olive oil from the oil cured sun-dried tomatoes in place of the 1 tablespoon called for in the ingredient list. Add 1 tablespoon fresh garlic tops, finely chopped (these are similar to chives with a hint of garlic flavor).

Per 1 cup serving: Calories 230, Protein 7 g., Fat 3 g., 12% fat (1% saturated fat), Carbohydrates 44 g., Dietary fiber trace, Cholesterol 0 mg., Sodium 136 mg., Calcium 25 mg., Iron 2 mg.
Exchanges: bread 2 1/2; vegetable 1/2; fat 1/2

EASY ONE POT PASTA

18 ounces pasta; mix it up, e.g.
  wheels, bows and spirals
Butter-flavored vegetable spray
  (or 1/4 teaspoon olive oil)
1 clove garlic, mashed
1 cup scallions, finely chopped
1 pound green beans
1 red pepper, cut julienne

2 cups sliced mushrooms
1/2 cup dry sherry
3 1/2 ounces soft Goat's cheese
3 ounces fat-free Philadelphia
  cream cheese
1/2 teaspoon salt (optional)
1/2 cup sun-dried tomatoes,
  softened, cut julienne

☐ Put 10-quart pot of water on to boil for pasta. In a heavy skillet coated with butter-flavored vegetable spray, sauté garlic and scallions until just transparent. Add green beans and cook a further 10 minutes, tossing from time to time. Add red pepper and sliced mushrooms and sauté over moderate heat. Add dry sherry about 5 minutes before the pasta is ready. Cook pasta in rapidly boiling lightly salted water, uncovered, until *al dente*. Before draining pasta, scoop out 1 cup of pasta water and purée it with cheeses. Drain pasta and toss with vegetables in sauté pan. Add julienned tomatoes and puréed cheeses, toss again and serve at once.

☐ Makes 8 servings.

Per serving: Calories 340, Protein 14 g., Fat 4 g., 11% fat (5% saturated fat),
  Carbohydrates 58 g., Dietary fiber 2 g., Cholesterol 13 mg., Sodium 262 mg.,
  Calcium 108 mg., Iron 4 mg.
Exchanges: vegetable 1 1/2; bread 3; meat 1/2; fat 1

EASY SPICY CAJUN PASTA WITH TOMATOES AND SHRIMP

1 tablespoon olive oil
1 large shallot, chopped finely
2 cloves of garlic, minced
3 ripe tomatoes, diced
3 tablespoons tomato paste

1/2 to 1 teaspoon Cajun spices
1 cup dry red wine
1 pound shrimp, peeled and deveined
Salt to taste (optional)
1 pound pasta

☐ Heat olive oil in a large sauté pan. Add shallots and garlic, reduce heat to medium-low and sauté until soft and transparent. Add diced tomatoes and cook for an additional 3 to 4 minutes. Stir in tomato paste, Cajun spices and dry red wine and bring to a boil; lower heat and simmer. Add shrimp and simmer for 5 minutes. Cook pasta in rapidly boiling water until *al dente*. Drain pasta and toss with sauce. Serve immediately.

☐ Makes 8 servings.

Per serving: Calories 330, Protein 21 g., Fat 4 g., 11% fat (1% saturated fat),
Carbohydrates 48 g., Dietary fiber 2 g., Cholesterol 87 mg., Sodium 141 mg.,
Calcium 43 mg., Iron 4 mg.
Exchanges: lean meat 1 1/2; bread 3; vegetables 1

LASAGNE WITH LEEKS AND RED PEPPERS

Vegetable cooking spray
1/2 teaspoon olive oil
3 to 4 cups leeks, diced
31/2 cups red pepper, sliced julienne
(11/2 to 2 peppers)
1 pound mushrooms, wiped clean
and sliced
1   (26-ounce) jar Classico *sweet
peppers & onions* pasta sauce or
Tomato & Basil
1   (8-ounce) can tomato sauce
(no added salt)

1/3 cup concentrated chicken stock*
1/2 cup (8 tablespoons) freshly
grated Parmesan cheese, divided
20 ounces skim milk ricotta cheese
(fat-free) (11/3 cartons)
1/2 to 1 teaspoon green peppercorns,
ground finely
1/2 teaspoon salt (optional)
2   (9-ounce) packages fresh
lasagne noodles (or enough
of your favorite noodles to make
4 layers)

☐ Preheat the oven to 350° F.

☐ Lightly oil a 14x11x2-inch lasagne pan with vegetable cooking spray.

☐ In a large skillet, warm the olive oil, add the leeks and sauté until they begin to sweat
and turn darker in color. Add the julienned red peppers, sauté for 3 to 4 minutes more,
then add the sliced mushrooms. Sauté another 6 to 8 minutes, or until the mushrooms
begin to exude their juices.

☐ Meanwhile, combine the Classico sauce with the tomato sauce; to expedite the
cooking time preheat to boiling before layering.

☐ Heat the chicken stock and blend it with half of the Parmesan cheese in a food
processor or blender. Add the ricotta, green peppercorns and optional salt and blend
until well combined.

☐ Lightly oil the lasagne pan with vegetable cooking spray.

☐ Pour a little red sauce over the bottom of the lasagne pan, then layer the ingredients
in the following order: noodles, sautéed veggies, red sauce, and cheese mixture. Be
sure to save enough red sauce and cheese to cover fairly evenly on the final layer.
Sprinkle the remaining Parmesan cheese on top.

☐ Cover with foil and bake in the middle of the preheated oven for 1 hour.

☐ Makes 8 servings.

☐ NOTE: *Homemade de-fatted salt free chicken stock tastes the best. Alternatively, use
Pritiken chicken broth. However, you will need to double the quantity and reduce it
down by boiling to get the best flavor. If you are vegetarian, a strong vegetable stock
also works well.

Per serving: Calories 348, Protein 24 g., Fat 8 g. 21% fat (10% saturated fat),
Carbohydrates 53 g., Dietary fiber 2 g., Cholesterol 11 mg., Sodium 690 mg.,
Calcium 78 mg., Iron 0.6 mg.
Exchanges: vegetable 2; bread 4; meat 1; fat 1

TOMATO PASTA WITH SHRIMP IN A SPICY RED SAUCE

1/4 **pound mushrooms, cleaned and thinly sliced**
1 **tablespoon extra virgin olive oil**
3 **medium cloves of garlic, green shoot removed and mashed**
1 **cup dry white wine**
1 **pound cocktail shrimp, thawed and drained if frozen**
2 **tablespoons fresh or frozen dill, finely chopped**

1 **(48-ounce) can tomato purée**
2 **teaspoons grated horseradish**
1/2 **teaspoon hot pepper sauce**
20 **ounces tomato pasta**
2 **ounces part-skim feta cheese, grated or ground in the food processor**
1 **ounce freshly grated part skim milk Parmesan cheese**

☐ Before you begin to cook, put the pasta water on to boil, set the table, and have your serving dish and colander ready to drain the pasta. Sauté the mushrooms in the olive oil over medium-high heat 3 to 4 minutes.

☐ Reduce heat and add the garlic; cook for another 4 to 5 minutes, then add the dry white wine and bring to a boil. Continue to boil for 4 to 5 minutes or until the volume is reduced by one-half.

☐ Add the shrimp and dill and reduce the heat to low. Cook until thoroughly heated.

☐ In a separate container, heat the tomato purée, horseradish and hot sauce; taste and adjust seasonings.

☐ Meanwhile, boil the pasta to al dente, then drain and toss with the cheeses.

☐ Add the tomato sauce to the shrimp, stir to combine and pour over the pasta. Serve at once. This is excellent accompanied by a tossed spinach salad.

☐ Makes 8 servings.

Per Serving: Calories 507, Protein 28 g., Fat 9 g., 16% fat (* saturated fat),
  Carbohydrates 77 g., Dietary fiber 4 g., Cholesterol 120 mg., Sodium 308 mg.,
  Calcium 158 mg., Iron 6 mg. *Data not available at this time.
Exchanges: lean meat 1; bread 4; vegetable 4; fat 1

CURRIED PASTA SALAD WITH SHRIMP AND ASPARAGUS

1 large shallot, finely chopped
3 cloves of garlic, shoot removed, finely minced
Juice of 1 lemon or to taste
*1 tablespoon lemon zest, finely chopped
1/4 cup olive oil
1/2 teaspoon salt (optional)
1 to 2 teaspoons curry powder
**1 pound shrimp (frozen uncooked work well), peeled and deveined
1 pound pasta, for more curry flavor use curry pasta

1 pound asparagus, cleaned and sliced diagonally into 2-inch lengths
1 cup nonfat plain yogurt
***2 sun-dried oil-cured tomatoes, cut into julienne strips
1/4 cup fresh coriander, coarsely chopped, or fresh parsley
1/4 cup sliced almonds, lightly roasted
Lemon slices and fresh coriander sprigs for garnish

□ Put a large pot of water on to boil for pasta. Combine shallot, garlic, lemon juice (add about 2 tablespoons initially and increase as desired when adjusting seasonings just before serving) and zest, olive oil, salt if desired, and curry powder. Mix well; set aside. Rinse shrimp under cold running water, then cook in boiling pasta water until just pink (usually by the time the water returns to the boil the shrimp are cooked). Remove shrimp with a slotted spoon and toss with shallot mixture. When pasta water returns to the boil, cook pasta until almost done. Add asparagus and continue to boil for 3 minutes or until pasta is *al dente*. Drain pasta, reserving 1/2 cup of pasta water, and toss with shrimp and shallot mixture. Whisk yogurt into the reserved pasta water and pour over pasta. Add sun-dried tomatoes and fresh coriander or parsley and toss well. Garnish with reserved shrimp, almonds, lemon slices and coriander sprigs and serve.

□ *Lemon zest is the outer peel of a lemon.

□ **If using unpeeled shrimp, reserve enough to garnish each serving.

□ ***To soften dried tomatoes, place in a steamer basket, steam for 10 minutes (as you would steam a vegetable). Place in an airtight container while still hot, store in refrigerator. Will keep *recipe ready* for months!

□ Makes 8 servings.

Per serving: Calories 417 g., Protein 24 g., Fat 13 g., 28% fat (3% saturated fat), Carbohydrates 52 g., Dietary fiber 1 mg., Cholesterol 88 mg., Sodium 112 mg., Calcium 134 mg., Iron 4 mg.
Exchanges: lean meat 1/2; vegetables 1; bread 3; fat 1

Scallions commonly known as green onions, are in the onion family. They have a strong flavor, particularly in the root ends. Use sparingly raw in salads. Best sautéed and added to pasta salads where they will not dominate. The green ends are shredded (cut diagonally) in Chinese cuisine and used as a garnish. This can work really well provided you don't overdo it.

FETTUCINI WITH SCALLOPS AND MUSSELS
IN SAFFRON SAUCE

12 ounces sea scallops (if large cut in half)
1 1/2 tablespoons olive oil
2 large shallots, peeled and finely chopped
1 cup bottled clam juice
1 cup dry vermouth
1 bunch of scallions, cleaned, trimmed to 6-inch lengths, finely chop white part, shred green tops and reserve
2 medium vine-ripened tomatoes, seeded and diced
1/3 teaspoon crumbled saffron threads

Freshly ground black pepper to taste
Salt to taste (optional)
1 pound fettucini pasta noodles
1 cup reserved pasta cooking water
5 ounces feta cheese
3 ounces freshly grated part-skim milk Parmesan cheese
30 mussels, scrubbed and debearded (substitute 1 pound medium shrimp* if desired, peeled and deveined)

☐ Put a large pot of water on to boil for the pasta.

☐ Cook the scallops gently in batches in the olive oil in sauté pan over medium heat until opaque, about 1 1/2 to 2 minutes; set aside.

☐ Add the shallots to the sauté pan with the clam juice and vermouth and boil for 6 to 7 minutes or until reduced by half its volume. Reduce the heat to moderate and add the scallion bottoms (white part), tomatoes, saffron, pepper and salt if desired. Cook for 5 minutes, stirring frequently.

☐ Meanwhile, cook the fettucini in the large pot of vigorously boiling lightly salted water until *al dente* (slightly underdone). Drain, reserving 1 cup, place in preheated serving dish. You need to time this to coincide with cooking the mussels and reheating the scallops. *If substituting shrimp, add them to the cooking pasta 5 minutes before it is cooked. Blend 1 cup of hot pasta water and cheeses in a food processor or blender until smooth and creamy.

☐ In a shallow pan with a lid, steam the mussels in 1 cup vigorously boiling water until they open, discard any that are cracked or that remain closed. These will only take 2 to 3 minutes, do not overcook, drain.

☐ Add the reserved scallops to the sauce and reheat gently. Remove from heat and stir in the cheese mixture, pour over drained pasta and toss well. Garnish with reserved green onion tops. Pile the mussels on top of the pasta and serve at once.

☐ Makes 8 servings.

Per serving: Calories 463, Protein 28 g., Fat 12 g., 23% fat (5% saturated fat), Carbohydrates 50 g., Dietary fiber 1 g., Cholesterol 53 mg., Sodium 620** mg., Calcium 270 mg., Iron 3 mg.   **Sodium information on clam juice not available, value actually higher.
Exchanges: lean meat 2 1/2; bread 3; vegetables 1; fat 1

PASTA SALAD WITH CHICKEN IN A TANGY CITRUS SAUCE

1 clove of garlic, shoot removed
and minced
2 teaspoons prepared hot mustard
1 teaspoon brown sugar
1 whole chicken breast, boned,
skinned, fat removed
(6 to 8 ounces)
1 medium Vidalia onion, diced, or 2
shallots
1 medium red pepper, seeded and
julienned
2 cups sliced mushrooms
2 large ripe tomatoes, seeded,
chopped
Juice and zest of 1/2 lemon
(3 tablespoons juice)

1/4 cup concentrated orange juice
(such as frozen concentrate)
Zest of 1 orange
3 tablespoons olive oil
2 tablespoons chopped fresh
rosemary (if unavailable use 1
teaspoon dried ground)
1 pound pasta, preferably spicy red
spirals
1/2 cup reserved pasta water
2 ounces crumbled blue cheese
such as roquefort or 3 ounces
freshly grated part skim milk
Parmesan cheese
1/2 teaspoon salt (optional)
2 teaspoons roasted sesame seed

☐ Combine garlic, mustard and brown sugar; mix well. Spread evenly over chicken. Broil 6 inches from heat for 5 minutes, turn and broil an additional 3 to 5 minutes. Allow to cool, then cut into bite-sized pieces, set aside.

☐ Combine onion, red pepper, mushrooms and tomatoes. Add lemon juice and zest, orange juice and zest, olive oil and rosemary. Stir well and marinate for 4 hours (all vegetables except mushrooms may be marinated overnight, add mushrooms anywhere between 4 hours to 15 minutes before cooking the pasta).

☐ Cook pasta in rapidly boiling lightly salted water until *al dente*. Just before the pasta is cooked, scoop out 1/2 cup of the pasta water and purée it with the cheese. When pasta is cooked, drain and toss with the puréed cheese, chicken and half of the marinated vegetables. Taste for seasoning and add optional salt if desired. Spoon the remainder of the marinated vegetables on top of the pasta and sprinkle with the sesame seeds. Serve warm or at room temperature.

☐ Makes 15 cups.

Per 2 Cup serving: Calories 389, Protein 19 g., Fat 10 g., 22% fat (2% saturated fat),
Carbohydrates 62 g., Dietary fiber 1 g., Cholesterol 26 mg., Sodium 312 mg.,
Calcium 84 mg., Iron 4 mg.
Exchanges: vegetable 1; bread 3; lean meat 1; fat 1

RICH AND CREAMY PASTA IN NUT SAUCE

1 pound pasta (spinach bows and
red pepper wagon wheels are our
favorites for this dish)
1 large shallot, finely chopped
(you can substitute 1/2 cup green
onions)
1 tablespoon olive oil
2 to 3 cloves of garlic, shoot
removed and finely chopped
1 large red pepper (1 to 2 cups),
julienned
1/4 pound pea pods, ends and
strings removed

51/2 ounces freshly grated part skim
milk Parmesan cheese
(1 heaping cup)
23/4 ounces chopped pecans
(1/2 cup plus 2 tablespoons)
1/3 cup Marsala or medium Sherry
Green part of 1 bunch of green
onions, shredded for garnish
1/4 cup fresh parsley, finely chopped
8 ounces fresh spinach leaves, well
washed to remove grit

☐ Put a large pot of water on to boil for the pasta. Sauté the shallots in olive oil in skillet over moderate heat until transparent, about 5 minutes. Add the garlic and continue to sauté 2 to 3 minutes. Add red pepper, sauté for a further few minutes until the pepper gives off some of its liquid.

☐ When the pasta water comes to a boil, add the pasta, cook, uncovered, to desired doneness. Add the pea pods to the sauté pan 5 minutes before the pasta is done.

☐ Combine the Parmesan and pecans in the food processor or blender; with the engine running, add 1 cup of hot pasta water and purée to a smooth consistency. Drain the pasta and toss with the cheese mixture. Add the Marsala to the sauté pan, return to a boil, then pour over the pasta, toss well. Garnish with the shredded onion and parsley. Serve at once on a bed of fresh spinach leaves.

☐ Makes 8 servings.

Variation: Omit the pea pods and add 1 head of broccoli flowerettes to the pasta water 5 minutes before the pasta is cooked.

Per serving: Calories 371, Protein 17 g., Fat 11 g., 27% fat (2% saturated fat),
Carbohydrates 52 g., Dietary fiber 4 g., Cholesterol 3 mg., Sodium 325 mg.,
Calcium 282 mg., Iron 3 mg.
Exchanges: meat 1; bread 3; vegetables 1; fat 1

Lean Meats & Marinades

DINNER IN A HURRY—BEEF STIR-FRY

1 teaspoon canola oil
1 pound lean thinly sliced sirloin
   (trimmed of all visible fat and cut
   into 1/4-inch strips)
1/2 pound mushrooms, wiped clean
   and thinly sliced
1 clove of garlic, shoot removed
   and mashed
1/2 teaspoon freshly grated
   ginger
1 tablespoon tamari sauce

4 scallions, white part chopped and
   green part shredded and kept
   separate, (1/4 cup)
1 teaspoon honey
2/3 cup freshly squeezed orange
   juice
2 teaspoons cornstarch
1 tablespoon water
1/4 cup fresh parsley or fresh leaf
   coriander, finely chopped
Orange slices

☐ Heat wok or sauté pan. Add the oil around the edges then add the beef. Stir-fry for about 3 minutes, then add the mushrooms, continue to cook a few more minutes then add the garlic, ginger, tamari and white part of the scallions. Stir-fry 2 to 3 more minutes.

☐ Add the green scallions, honey and orange juice and bring to a boil. Dissolve cornstarch in water and add to beef mixture. Bring to a boil and cook 1 minute stirring constantly. Serve at once garnished with fresh parsley and an orange slice. This is excellent served over one of the whole grain Lundberg rices accompanied by steamed green vegetables in season.

☐ Makes 4 servings.

Per serving: Calories 228, Protein 27 g., Fat 8 g., 32% fat (9% saturated fat), Carbohydrates 13 g., Dietary fiber 2 g., Cholesterol 68 mg., Sodium 224 mg., Calcium 29 mg., Iron 5 mg.
Exchanges: lean meat 3 1/2; fruit 1/2; vegetables 1

GRILLED BUTTERFLIED LEG OF LAMB

1 to 2 minced garlic cloves
1/2 cup dry vermouth
2 teaspoons olive oil
1/4 cup prepared Dijon-style
  mustard
2 tablespoons Worcestershire sauce

2 tablespoons fresh rosemary,
  finely chopped
1/4 cup lemon juice
1/2 leg of lamb, boned, fat removed,
  butterflied

☐ Combine first 7 ingredients in a jar and shake well. Place leg of lamb in a shallow dish. Open out the leg of lamb, score the surface and pour marinade over, turning to be sure it is well coated. Marinate overnight in refrigerator. Remove lamb from marinade. Grill 4 inches above the coals of a moderately hot fire, about 20 minutes per side. To broil place 4 inches from the broiler for about 8 to 10 minutes per side depending on the thickness and your preference. Allow 10 minutes resting time after meat is cooked before carving, this allows the meat to firm up and continue to cook a little. Great with steamed new potatoes and pea pods.

☐ Makes 6 servings.

Per serving: Calories 202, Protein 24 g., Fat 8 g., 36% fat (* saturated fat),
  Carbohydrates 3 g., Dietary fiber 0 g., Cholesterol 80 mg., Sodium 180 mg.,
  Calcium 37 mg., Iron 4 mg. *Data not available at this time.
Exchanges: lean meat 3 1/2

BROILED OR GRILLED PORK TENDERLOIN

1 1/2 pounds pork tenderloin,
  trimmed of all visible fat
1/2 a recipe Piquant and Fruity
  Marinade (see page 97)

Prepared sweet mustard

☐ Prepare fire or preheat broiler. Marinate tenderloin for 2 to 4 hours or overnight in refrigerator. Remove from marinade. Grill or broil 6 inches from heat until internal temperature registers 160° F., turning once. This usually takes around 8 to 10 minutes, depending on the thickness. You can also test for doneness by pressing the meat with your fingers, it springs back when cooked. Allow to stand 10 minutes prior to carving. Reheat any leftover marinade and pour over meat. Carve into 1/2-inch slices and serve with steamed new potatoes and a tossed green salad. Pass the prepared mustard.

☐ Makes 6 servings.

Per serving: Calories 214, Protein 33 g., Fat 7 g., 29% fat (8% saturated fat),
  Carbohydrates 4 g., Dietary fiber trace, Cholesterol 105 mg., Sodium 180 mg.,
  Calcium 13 mg., Iron 2 mg.
Exchanges: lean meat 5; fat (-2); (fruit 1/2–may be discarded with marinade)

A MEDLEY OF MARINADES

Marinades are one of the great liberators in the kitchen. Assemble several batches of different meats in marinades in your freezer for a quick grill. They will last up to three months, and provide a quick and easy meal after a long day at the office. The marinades will also freeze independently in ice cube containers; thaw in a plastic bag under the hot tap, or in the microwave oven. We keep ours in one-batch amounts in ziplock bags, labelled, and placed inside another bag, for easy identification. To use simply thaw out the marinade, then add the meat directly into the bag. If you do this before going to work in the morning, and if it's going to be marinating for more than 4 hours, store it in the refrigerator. Fish needs only to marinate ½ to 1 hour. Remember to remove all chicken skin and visible fat prior to marinating. Baste the meat with its marinade during the cooking.

General Guidelines:

☐ Remove all visible fat from the meat, skin all poultry.

☐ Combine all ingredients in a ziplock plastic bag or a container with a tight fitting lid large enough to hold the meat and marinade. If there are any instructions relating to a specific marinade, they will be included with that recipe.

☐ Add the meat to the marinade, turning it to surround the meat with the marinade. Turn the meat several more times as it marinates. If using a plastic bag, you need only turn the bag over.

☐ Marinate meat at room temperature 2 to 4 hours or overnight in the refrigerator.

☐ Grill or broil meat and or fish 4 inches from the heat source. Timing will depend upon the density of the meat, whether you like it rare, medium or well done and the type of meat. Pork must be cooked to an internal temperature of 160° F. Chicken is done when the juices run clear when pierced at the thickest part with a fork. Fish takes 10 minutes per inch judging from the thickest part of the fish. Heat of the coals will also depend on the type of meat being used. Beef requires a very hot fire, pork and chicken moderately hot in order to cook the meat all the way through without burning the outside. Fish usually takes a fairly hot fire, although not as hot as beef.

☐ Brush the meat with the marinade several times during cooking. For a quick sauce, heat leftover marinade to boiling, thicken with cornstarch as desired and pour it over the cooked meat.

☐ NOTE: A portion of the fat and fruit exchanges will be discarded with unused marinade.

TAMARI MARINADE

2 cloves of garlic, crushed
1/4 cup tamari sauce
2 tablespoons apple cider
1/4 cup dry white wine

1/4 teaspoon grated fresh ginger
1/2 teaspoon brown sugar
3 whole chicken breasts, skinned,
 fat removed

☐ Combine first 6 ingredients. Marinate and cook chicken according to general directions (page 96).

☐ Makes 6 servings.

☐ NOTE: Great with swordfish, marlin, fresh tuna or lean pork. It can also be used as a sauce.

Per serving: Calories 105, Protein 20 g., Fat 1 g., 9% fat (3% saturated fat),
 Carbohydrates 1 g., Dietary fiber 0 g., Cholesterol 49 mg., Sodium 456 mg.,
 Calcium 13 mg., Iron 1 mg.
Exchanges: lean meat 3; fat (-2)

PIQUANT AND FRUITY MARINADE FOR POULTRY

1 tablespoon olive oil
2 tablespoons Raspberry Vinegar
 (page 67)
2 tablespoons low-sodium soy sauce
2 to 3 tablespoons boysenberry
 syrup or other berry syrup or
 concentrated fruit juice

Juice and zest of 1 lemon
3 cloves of garlic, shoot removed
 and mashed
3 whole chicken breasts, skinned,
 fat removed or 2 boneless turkey
 breasts

☐ Combine first 6 ingredients. Marinate and cook chicken or turkey according to general directions (page 96).

☐ Makes 6 servings.

Per serving: Calories 148, Protein 20 g., Fat 3 g., 18% fat (4% saturated fat),
 Carbohydrates 10 g., Dietary fiber 0 g., Cholesterol 49 mg., Sodium 263 mg.,
 Calcium 19 mg., Iron 1 mg.
Exchanges: lean meats 3; (fruit 1/2–may be discarded with marinade); fat (-1)

MARINATED FLANK STEAK

Rum Soy Sauce:

3 tablespoons dark rum
3 tablespoons low-sodium soy sauce

2 cloves of garlic, crushed
1¹/₂ pounds lean flank steak

☐ Combine rum, soy sauce and garlic in a saucepan, bring to a boil. Cool. Add flank steak and marinate overnight. Grill according to general directions.

☐ Makes 6 servings. (photo page 65)

☐ NOTE: Good for lamb, pork or turkey. For shishkabob try cutting up the meat and skewering alternately with pearl onions, button mushrooms, red pepper squares and cherry tomatoes.

Per serving: Calories 224, Protein 22 g., Fat 13 g., 52% fat (24% saturated fat),
Carbohydrates 0 g., Dietary fiber 0 g., Cholesterol 60 mg., Sodium 370 mg.,
Calcium 7 mg., Iron 2 mg.
Exchanges: meat 3; fat 1

GREEN PEPPERCORNS AND LIME SAUCE

"Great over poultry or seafood"

¹/₄ cup sweet marsala
¹/₂ cup concentrated poultry stock
(made from the carcass of the
game or ducks if accompanying
them)
2 to 3 tablespoons lime juice
Zest of 1 lime

1 to 2 tablespoons freeze-dried
green peppercorns, finely ground
or to taste
2 teaspoons arrowroot (or
cornstarch)
2 teaspoons water

☐ Combine the marsala and stock, bring to a boil and cook until reduced to 1 cup.

☐ Add the lime juice and zest and green peppercorns, return to a boil.

☐ Dissolve arrowroot in water. Remove sauce from the heat and stir in the arrowroot, pour over the meat and serve, or pass in a sauce boat. (If you substitute cornstarch be sure to return to a boil after adding it as it will not thicken otherwise.)

☐ Makes 6 servings.

Per 2 tablespoon serving: Calories 22, Protein 0 g., Fat trace, Carbohydrates 3 g.,
Dietary fiber 0 g., Cholesterol 0 mg., Sodium 2 mg., Calcium 6 mg., Iron trace.
Exchanges: free

VEGETABLES & SIDE DISHES

A Variety of Vegetables on the Grill
page 101

Broiled Norwegian Salmon
page 82

French Baguettes
page 57

Frozen Yogurt Fruit Pie
page 130

Per serving for complete menu: Calories, 703, Protein 39 g.,
Fat 22 g. (total = 28% saturated = 4%), Carbohydrates 87 g.,
Dietary fiber 9 g., Cholesterol 81 mg., Sodium 450 mg.,
Calcium 217 mg., Iron 4 mg.

Side dishes enhance the entree and add texture and color to the plate. To ensure the best flavor and highest nutrient value purchase the freshest, ripest produce available. For further information on selecting produce at its optimum freshness contact your local cooperative extension service. Many of these side dishes can be transformed into a main course or matched up with a salad for a complete meal.

Photograph: A Variety of Vegetables on the Grill, page 101

A VARIETY OF VEGETABLES ON THE GRILL

Little packages of marinated vegetables wrapped in aluminum foil and placed on the grill make an interesting and novel presentation to accompany chicken or fish at a cookout. Allow one cup vegetables per person.

Broccoli flowerettes

Cauliflower flowerettes

2-inch lengths of green onions

Button mushrooms

Asparagus, cut on diagonal, 2-inch
  lengths

2-inch lengths of green beans

Baby zucchini cut into 2-inch
  lengths (cut in half or quartered
  if large)

Cherry tomatoes, pierced with a
  fork

New potatoes (little ones, pierced a
  few times)

Red, green or yellow peppers, cut
  into 1 1/2-inch squares

Mrs. Dash (as desired)

Freshly ground pepper (as desired)

Salt (optional)

☐ Marinate the above vegetables in your favorite dressing for 1 to 2 hours, we suggest our Lemonette Dressing. Allow 1 tablespoon of dressing per cup of vegetables. Season to your preference.

☐ The best way to deal with personal preferences is to have a couple of cups of each vegetable (the above are only suggestions) marinating in separate containers near a work station. The vegetables should marinate for at least an hour. Pre-cut squares of heavy duty aluminum foil and let your guests make their own packages. Suggested cooking time 5 minutes on the grill, turning once, except for the potatoes which will take 20 to 30 minutes depending on their size. If desired, the vegetables may be broiled for 6 to 8 minutes, turning once.

☐ NOTE: Whole vegetables may be placed on skewers directly on the grill.

Lemonette Dressing

2 tablespoons lemon juice

1/2 cup orange juice

1/3 cup virgin olive oil

2 cloves of garlic, shoot removed
  and mashed

1 tablespoon fresh rosemary or
  fresh herb of choice, finely
  chopped

☐ Combine all ingredients in a jar and shake vigorously. Use as marinade for grilled vegetables.

☐ Makes 1 cup. (photo page 99)

Per 1 cup serving: Calories 102, Protein 3 g., Fat 3 g., 26% fat (4% saturated fat),
  Carbohydrates 16 g., Dietary fiber 4 g., Cholesterol 0 mg., Sodium 51 mg.,
  Calcium 32 mg., Iron 2 mg.

Exchanges: bread 1/2; vegetable 1; fat 1/2

EASY POTATO WEDGES

A family favorite alternative to French fries with only a fraction of the fat!

**6 medium potatoes (redskins,
   golden Yukons, white or Idaho)
Butter-flavored vegetable spray**

**1/2 teaspoon seasoned salt*,
   optional, or 1/2 teaspoon butter-
   flavored granules****

- ☐ Preheat oven to 400° F.

- ☐ Thoroughly scrub potatoes, and remove any dark spots or *eyes*. Microwave at 100% power for 5 to 7 minutes, or until just underdone.

- ☐ Cut into fourths, and place skin side down on a lightly sprayed cookie sheet. ***Lightly spray potatoes with the vegetable spray, and sprinkle with optional seasoned salt or butter-flavored granules. Bake in preheated oven for 15 minutes, or until golden.

- ☐ Makes 6 servings.

- ☐ NOTES: *The sodium has been calculated using 1/2 teaspoon salt. **Such as butter buds or Molly McButter. ***The fat has been calculated using 2 seconds of spraying time when spraying the potatoes with butter-flavored vegetable spray.

Per serving: Calories 110, Protein 3 g., Fat trace, 2% fat (trace saturated fat), Carbohydrates 25 g., Dietary fiber 4 g., Cholesterol 0 mg., Sodium 191* mg., (94 mg. if using butter-flavored granules instead of seasoning salt), Calcium 19 mg., Iron 2 mg.
Exchanges: bread 1 1/2

PURÉE OF SWEET POTATOES WITH YOGURT AND NUTMEG

**2 pounds sweet potatoes
1 cup plain nonfat yogurt**

**1/4 teaspoon freshly grated nutmeg
   or to taste**

- ☐ Preheat oven to 400° F. Bake the sweet potatoes until tender, about 45 minutes; peel.

- ☐ To cook in the microwave, wrap potatoes individually in paper towels, cook on High for 15 to 20 minutes.

- ☐ Combine the potatoes and yogurt in the food processor or blender, process until smooth.

- ☐ Fold in 1/4 teaspoon freshly grated nutmeg. Serve in warmed dish with nutmeg grated on top. This will hold very well in a 300° F. oven for at least an hour, or until ready to serve.

- ☐ Makes 8 servings (photo page 109).

Per serving: Calories 132, Protein 4 g., Fat trace, Carbohydrates 30 g., Dietary fiber 3 g., Cholesterol trace, Sodium 33 mg., Calcium 88 mg., Iron 0.5 mg.
Exchanges: bread 2

SPICY BAKED FANNED EGGPLANT

2 teaspoons olive oil
6 tablespoons fresh lemon-thyme (frozen or dry regular thyme can be substituted, use 1/3 the quantity)
2 teaspoons coriander seeds, roasted and finely ground
3 large shallots, finely chopped
3 cloves of garlic, finely chopped (shoot removed)
3 ounces dried mushrooms such as cepes or boletus or porcini (substitute 8 ounces fresh if dry unavailable)

Salt and pepper to taste
3 medium fresh ripe eggplants
2 mild onions, sliced
4 ounces sun-dried tomatoes (oil-packed) julienned (or 1 1/2 ounce dried)
1 yellow pepper (if yellow unavailable, substitute red) seeded and cut julienne
1 red pepper, seeded and cut julienne
Juice of 1 lemon
1/2 cup ripe olives (optional)

- ☐ Spread the olive oil over the bottom of a large rectangular baking dish (large enough to hold all the eggplants halved and placed side by side).

- ☐ Distribute half of the lemon thyme, coriander, shallots, garlic and dried mushrooms over the bottom of the dish plus salt and pepper to taste.

- ☐ Cut each eggplant in half, and remove the stem end then slice vertically at 1/6 inch intervals (taking care not to cut all the way down to the narrow end) then set in the baking dish, flat side down. Insert the onion slices and julienne sun-ripened tomatoes in between the slices, sprinkle with remaining lemon-thyme, coriander, shallots, garlic and dried mushrooms.

- ☐ Arrange the julienned red and yellow peppers on top, sprinkle with pepper to taste. Bake, loosely covered with foil in a preheated 375° F. oven for 1 hour. Add lemon juice and olives, cover and bake an additional 20 minutes.

- ☐ Makes 6 servings.

Per serving: Calories 74, Protein 2 g., Fat 3 g., 36% fat (6% saturated fat), Carbohydrates 12 g., Dietary fiber 6 g., Cholesterol 0 mg., Sodium 50 mg., Calcium 68 mg., Iron 3.7 mg.
Exchanges: vegetables 2; fat 1/2

Basic Methods for Steaming Vegetables

Microwave or stovetop steaming: This method uses the steam from rapidly boiling water to cook the vegetables, and most pots which go on top of the stove, or in the microwave can be adapted with the use of an inexpensive metal or plastic insert which elevates the vegetables above the water, yet allows the steam through. The universal time for this cooking method seems to be around 5 to 6 minutes for tender firm results, allowing a little more for thick stems and or a little less for delicate vegetables.

QUICK ZUCCHINI STIR-FRY

1 teaspoon olive oil
1 clove of garlic, shoot removed
  and minced
6 to 7 medium zucchini, scrubbed
  and cut into 2-inch julienne

1 tablespoon tomato paste
1 tablespoon red wine vinegar
2 tablespoons fresh parsley,
  chopped finely
1/4 teaspoon salt (optional)

☐ Heat the olive oil in a heavy skillet to medium heat, add the garlic and sauté until transparent. Add the zucchini and when it has released some of its juices add tomato paste and vinegar, heat to boiling. Toss with the fresh parsley and salt if desired. Serve immediately.

☐ Makes 6 servings.

Per serving: Calories 28, Protein 2 g., Fat 1 g., 32% fat (4% saturated fat), Carbohydrates 5 g., Dietary fiber 2 g., Cholesterol 0 mg., Sodium 97 mg., Calcium 141 mg., Iron 4 mg.
Exchanges: vegetables 1

LEMON BROCCOLI WITH GOMASIO
(ROASTED SESAME SALT)

1 bunch broccoli, washed, cut into
  spears
Juice of 1/2 lemon

1/2 teaspoon olive oil
1 tablespoon Gomasio (roasted
  sesame seed and salt condiment)

☐ Steam broccoli for 5 to 6 minutes, until tender but firm. Remove and place on warmed serving plate. Combine lemon juice and oil, sprinkle over broccoli. Sprinkle 1 tablespoon gomasio over broccoli and serve immediately.

☐ Makes 6 servings. (photo page 109)

Per serving: Calories 34, Protein 3 g., Fat 1 g., 26% fat (4% saturated fat), Carbohydrates 5 g., Dietary fiber 4 g., Cholesterol 0 mg., Sodium 65 mg., Calcium 51 mg., Iron 0.9 mg.
Exchanges: vegetable 1

Agnes Orringer's Gomasio
1/2 cup sesame seeds   1 teaspoon sea salt

☐ Sort and wash seeds. Using a cast iron skillet if possible, roast salt to thoroughly dry (about 1 minute), remove from pan. Add the sesame seeds and roast until they pop, or turn light golden in color. Grind with the salt in a suribachi or mortar and pestle, in several batches.

☐ Makes 8 tablespoons.

RATATOUILLE

1 large eggplant (4 to 5 cups), diced
3 medium zucchini, diced (3 cups)
1 teaspoon olive oil
1 large onion or 2 medium (3 cups), diced
2 cloves of garlic, shoot removed and mashed
1 teaspoon Szechuan pepper (available in oriental markets or specialty food stores), lightly roasted

1 teaspoon coriander seeds, lightly roasted and ground
1 large red or yellow pepper, cut into 1-inch squares
2 ripe tomatoes, diced (2 1/2 cups)
1   14 1/2-ounce can tomato purée
1 tablespoon red wine vinegar
1/2 cup fresh basil, coarsely chopped
Hot pepper sauce (optional)

☐ Cook the eggplant in the microwave with 1/4 cup water for 5 minutes on High, or blanch in rapidly boiling water, drain. Repeat the procedure with the zucchini reducing the cooking time to 3 minutes.

☐ In a large Dutch oven, heat the olive oil and sauté the onion until transparent, about 5 minutes. Add the garlic and sauté a few more minutes. Add the Szechuan peppers and coriander.

☐ Add the eggplant and zucchini and remaining ingredients to the onions except the fresh basil and pepper sauce. Bring to a boil, reduce heat and simmer for 50 minutes. Add the basil and simmer an additional 10 minutes. Adjust seasonings and add a dash of hot pepper sauce if desired.

☐ Makes 8 servings.

Serving Suggestions:

— as a vegetable side dish with seafood or grilled chicken

— as a main course over rice with grated part skim milk Parmesan cheese on top

— on a baked potato

— cold in a pita pocket at a picnic

— with double the tomato purée as a sauce over pasta

Per serving: Calories 95, Protein 4 g., Fat 1 g., 9% fat (2% saturated fat),
Carbohydrates 17 g., Dietary fiber 6 g., Cholesterol 0 mg., Sodium 19 mg.,
Calcium 58 mg., Iron 1.7 mg.
Exchanges: vegetables 3

VERSATILE AND DELICIOUS REFRIED BEANS

From Agnes Orringer's Kitchen

1 onion, chopped
1/2 green pepper, chopped
1 to 2 stalks celery, chopped
1 to 2 carrots, scrubbed clean and
  chopped
1 tablespoon sesame oil

1   (48-ounce) can pinto beans
1 to 2 tablespoons fresh parsley,
  chopped
Tamari, barley miso or low-sodium
  soy sauce to taste

☐ In a large heavy skillet, sauté the fresh vegetables in the sesame oil on moderately low heat to avoid burning the oil.

☐ Chop the beans coarsely either pulsing in the food processor or with a potato masher, add them to the vegetable mixture, cover and simmer for 5 minutes. Uncover and bring to a boil, stirring constantly. Cook until the liquid is reduced and a creamy texture is achieved. Remove from heat and stir in parsley and season with tamari.

☐ Makes 12 servings.

Per serving: Calories 136, Protein 7 g., Fat 2 g., 13% fat (1% saturated fat),
  Carbohydrates 23 g., Dietary fiber 8 g., Cholesterol 0 mg., Sodium 382 mg.,
  Calcium 27 mg., Iron 2 mg.
Exchanges: lean meat 1/2; bread 1 1/2

BAKED BEANS WITH APPLES AND LEEKS

1 pound navy beans
1 pound (2 bunches) leeks, white
  part only, thoroughly washed and
  chopped
4 large tart cooking apples, peeled,
  cored and sliced

1 1/3 cups cider or apple juice
1/3 cup honey
2 tablespoons molasses
1/2 cup chopped fresh parsley
Hot sauce to taste (optional)
2 tablespoons barley miso

☐ Rinse, sort and soak beans in water to cover overnight. Drain beans, discarding liquid. Combine beans with next 5 ingredients in a large Dutch oven. Bring to a boil, cover tightly, and bake at 300° F. until tender and leeks and apple are no longer identifiable, 4 to 6 hours. Stir in the chopped parsley and hot sauce if desired. Stir in the barley miso, taste and adjust seasonings as desired.

☐ Makes 8 cups.

☐ NOTE: These beans freeze well.

Per serving: Calories 161, Protein 7 g., Fat 1 g., 6% fat (1% saturated fat),
  Carbohydrates 34 g., Dietary fiber 6 g., Cholesterol 0 mg., Sodium 92 mg.,
  Calcium 79 mg., Iron 3 mg.
Exchanges: bread 1; vegetable 1; fruit 1

EASY RICE PILAF

1½ cups uncooked brown rice or ¾ cup brown and ¾ cup wild 3 cups diced onions 2 teaspoons olive oil 1 to 2 cloves of garlic, minced	1½ cups grated carrots 2 cups sliced mushrooms 1 cup diced tomato Dash of hot sauce 2 tablespoons low-sodium soy sauce

☐ Place the rice on to cook according to package directions. (To cook rice in the microwave, combine rice, 3 cups water, and a pinch of salt if desired. Microwave on High for 10 minutes, reduce to 50% power and microwave an additional 25 minutes.)

☐ Sauté the onion in a heavy skillet in the olive oil over low heat, add the garlic and continue to cook a few minutes more. Add the carrots and mushrooms, and as soon as they give off some liquid increase the heat to medium, stirring constantly. Cook an additional 5 minutes.

☐ When the rice is cooked, toss it in with the vegetables plus any liquid in the bottom of the pan, add the tomato, hot sauce and soy sauce. Just before serving, broil for 2 to 3 minutes or until edges are crisp. Great served with Lightly Breaded (Oat Bran) Chicken Breasts and Lemon Mushroom Sauce (page 70).

☐ Makes 8 servings.

Per serving: Calories 174, Protein 4 g., Fat 2 g., 10% fat (1% saturated fat),
  Carbohydrates 35 g., Dietary fiber 6 g., Cholesterol 0 mg., Sodium 163 mg.,
  Calcium 35 mg., Iron 1 mg.
Exchanges: bread 2; vegetable 1

FRESH FRUIT SALAD

1 cup seedless grapes, cut in half 1 pint fresh strawberries, wiped clean and cut in half 1 cup honeydew melon	1 cup fresh pineapple chunks 1 cup fresh blueberries Juice of ½ lemon Fresh mint sprigs, optional garnish

☐ Wash all fruit in fresh running water before cutting it up. Combine all prepared fruit in a large serving bowl with the lemon juice, toss well. Garnish with fresh mint sprigs.

☐ Makes 6 servings.

Variations: Six cups favorite fresh fruit in season would have comparable calories.

Per serving: Calories 63, Protein 1 g., Fat 1 g., 7% fat (trace saturated fat),
  Carbohydrates 16 g., Dietary fiber 3 g., Cholesterol 0 mg., Sodium 4 mg.,
  Calcium 15 mg., Iron 0.4 mg.
Exchanges: fruit 1

GAIL AND NEIL'S EGGPLANT WITH BLACK BEANS

Great as an appetizer, or an accompaniment to a Chinese meal

1 medium eggplant, cut into
   1/2-inch dice
2 teaspoons canola oil
2 tablespoons fermented black
   beans, chopped
1 teaspoon ginger, grated
1 clove of garlic, shoot removed,
   chopped finely

1 tablespoon oyster sauce
1 tablespoon light soy sauce
1 1/2 teaspoons red wine vinegar
1/2 teaspoon sugar
1/2 teaspoon hot chili oil (found in
   oriental section)
1 chopped scallion (green part only)

☐ Sprinkle eggplant lightly with salt and place in a colander. Drain for 30 minutes then remove excess moisture with a paper towel. Set aside. Heat wok over medium heat until the top edges are hot to the touch, then drizzle in the oil from the top of the wok. When the oil is very hot add the black beans, ginger, garlic and stir fry for 1 minute.

☐ Add the reserved eggplant and continue to stir fry vigorously to prevent the eggplant from sticking to the wok. When the eggplant is transparent, add the oyster sauce, soy sauce and vinegar, and stir-fry 1 to 2 minutes or until heated through. Stir in the sugar and hot chili oil and garnish with scallions.

☐ Makes 4 servings.

☐ NOTE: Salting the eggplant prior to cooking removes any bitterness which can occur. Omit this step if you are on a sodium restricted diet.

Per serving: Calories 82, Protein 2 g., Fat 3 g., 33% fat (3% saturated fat),
   Carbohydrates 6 g., Dietary fiber 5 g., Cholesterol 0 mg., Sodium 302 mg.,
   Calcium 31 mg., Iron trace.
Exchanges: vegetable 1; fat 1/2

CORN ON THE COB ON THE GRILL

Ear of corn per person, still in
   its husk
Lemon wedges

Salt and freshly ground pepper to
   taste

☐ Cover corn with water and allow to soak for 30 minutes. Drain. Place the corn on the grill about 6 inches from the coals, turning every 5 to 10 minutes, for 30 minutes or until the husks are tinged with brown and the corn tender. Remove from the grill. Remove the husks and silk just before serving. Pass the lemon wedges and seasoning.

☐ Makes one ear of corn per person.

Per serving: Calories 61, Protein 2 g., Fat trace, Carbohydrates 15 g., Dietary fiber 5 g.,
   Cholesterol 0 mg., Sodium 3 mg., Calcium 4 mg., Iron 0.4 mg.
Exchanges: bread 1

SPECIAL OCCASIONS

Crudité Platter with an Assortment of Dips
page 42

Roast Breast of Turkey Roll with High Fiber Dressing
page 111

Festive Cranberry Conserve
page 118

Purée of Sweet Potatoes with Yogurt and Nutmeg
page 102

Lemon Broccoli with Gomasio
page 104

Light and Fluffy Potato Bread with Oat Bran
page 59

Pear Raspberry Tart
page 139

Cranberry Punch
page 43

Per serving for complete menu: Calories, 1126, Protein 72 g.,
Fat 27 g. (total = 22% saturated = 3%), Carbohydrates 151 g.,
Dietary fiber 23 g., Cholesterol 113 mg., Sodium 961 mg.,
Calcium 399 mg., Iron 11 mg.

During the holidays or at other special occasions, tradition and adherence to old habits make it difficult for us to make changes. This chapter introduces you to exciting menu ideas for that special event. In addition, there are endless combinations of recipes that you can select to fulfill any party fare. Remember when entertaining to choose recipes that can be prepared in advance. You will see many little "do ahead tips" within the texts of our recipes to help with timing for your party preparations.

Photograph: Roast Breast of Turkey Roll with High Fiber Dressing, Purée of Sweet
Potatoes with Yogurt and Nutmeg, Festive Cranberry Conserve,
Lemon Broccoli with Gomasio, pages 111, 102, 118 and 104

ROAST BREAST OF TURKEY ROLL
WITH HIGH FIBER STUFFING

2½ to 3 pounds turkey breast,
  boned
2 to 3 teaspoons Dijon-style
  mustard
½ teaspoon salt (optional)
Fresh ground pepper to taste
2 to 3 medium-sized shallots, finely
  chopped
1 tablespoon plus 1 teaspoon of
  olive oil

2 medium-sized cloves of garlic,
  shoot removed and finely chopped
1¼ pounds fresh mushrooms,
  wiped clean
10 ounces fresh spinach, washed,
  steamed
⅓ cup dry vermouth
¼ cup chopped walnuts
⅓ cup oat bran

☐ Skin and defat the turkey breast, also defat the skin by scraping the underside with a sharp flexible knife such as a boning knife to remove any visible fat, and reserve. Slice the thick end of the turkey breast horizontally, and open it out to increase its surface areas. Score with a sharp knife then spread with mustard, sprinkle with salt if desired and pepper and set aside.

☐ Sauté the shallots over low heat in 1 tablespoon olive oil until transparent, about 5 minutes, add the garlic and continue to cook an additional 5 minutes.

☐ Chop 8 ounces of the mushrooms, plus the stems from the remaining mushrooms, and add them to the sauté pan. Reserve the remaining caps to stuff.

☐ Drain the spinach by pressing out the liquid through a sieve, then chop and add it to the sauté pan, cook 2 to 3 minutes. Stir in the dry vermouth, walnuts and oat bran, cook a few more minutes to heat through.

☐ Preheat oven to 375° F. Spread the stuffing ½-inch thick over the surface of the turkey breast stuffing within ½ inch edges (this usually takes about 1 to 1½ cups of the stuffing). Reserve the remaining stuffing. Roll the breast, (not too tight) and wrap it in the defatted skin. Secure it with kitchen twine and rub with the reserved 1 teaspoon olive oil to moisten the skin prior to roasting. Lower oven heat to 325° F. and roast turkey roll for approximately 1 hour and 15 minutes, (35 minutes per pound) or until the juices run clear when pierced with a fork. When the roast has cooked, allow it to rest 10 minutes out of the oven, this facilitates carving. Remove twine and skin prior to carving. Serve with Turkey Gravy (page 112).

☐ Makes 8 servings. (photo page 109)

☐ Recipe continued on page 112.

TURKEY GRAVY

Defatted liquid from roasting pan*
1/4 cup dry vermouth
1/2 teaspoon salt or to taste
  (optional)
1/2 cup defatted reduced-sodium
  chicken stock

2 teaspoons cornstarch
1 tablespoon cold water
2 tablespoons low-sodium soy sauce
1/2 teaspoon Kitchen Bouquet
  (gravy seasoning) to taste

☐ Combine first 4 ingredients and bring to a boil. Combine cornstarch, water and soy sauce. Add Kitchen Bouquet to taste. Add to stock mixture and return to a boil. Boil 1 minute.

☐ Serve separately in a sauce boat.

*To defat the liquid from the roasting pan pour it, plus the other liquids into a "skimmer jug" (this has the spout coming from the bottom), allow to stand until you see the fat floating on top. Carefully pour the liquid out of the jug until you reach the fat, discard the fat. Proceed with the recipe.

Spinach-Stuffed Mushroom Caps

☐ Fill the reserved mushroom caps (usually 20 to 25) with the reserved stuffing and broil for 5 minutes, coordinate the time to have them done when the turkey is ready to carve.

Per serving: Calories 304, Protein 46 g., Fat 6 g., 18% fat (3% saturated fat),
  Carbohydrates 10 g., Dietary fiber 4 g., Cholesterol 106 mg., Sodium 515 mg.,
  Calcium 71 mg., Iron 4 mg.
Exchanges: lean meat 6; bread 1/2; vegetable 1; fat (-2)

Ice Ring

In a circular ice mold half full of water, place lemon twists, orange twists, mint leaves and marachino cherries in an attractive pattern. Carefully place this in the freezer so as not to disturb your arrangement. Freeze until solid (you should check periodically that the fruit has not migrated as it freezes and rearrange it accordingly.) When frozen solid, fill the mold to the top with more water and freeze solid This looks very festive floating in a punch bowl.

ENTERTAINING MEATLESS

*Hummus with an Assortment of
Dipping Veggies
page 39*

*Tossed Salad Greens with
Lemonette Dressing
page 101*

*Meatless Lasagna with
Mushrooms and Spinach
page 114*

*Hearty Mixed Grain Bread
page 58*

*Strawberry Rhubarb Crumble
page 134*

Per serving for complete menu:
Calories 1036, Protein 44 g.,
Fat 22 g. (total = 18% saturated = 5%),
Carbohydrates, 179 g.,
Dietary fiber 18 g., Cholesterol 22 mg.,
Sodium 841 mg., Calcium 640 mg.,
Iron 11 mg.

Key Points for All Entertaining:

- Plan details ahead, it is often good to put these down on paper
  Who is coming? (send out invitations or call)
  What is the party theme?
  Where will the party be held?
  Who will do the work?

- Keep to your budget

- Be creative with your table settings and color schemes

- Clean your house two days before (or at least the day before)

- Set your table the day before

- Arrange your foods, plates and napkins in logical order

- Take time out before your guests arrive to shower, dress and
  relax so you enjoy your party.

MEATLESS LASAGNA WITH MUSHROOMS AND SPINACH

1/4 ounce dry mushrooms (boletus, cepes or porcini) or 4 ounces extra fresh mushrooms
1/4 cup dry vermouth
1 teaspoon olive oil
1 large shallot, finely chopped
3 to 4 cloves of garlic, minced
1 pound fresh mushrooms, sliced
1 tablespoon green peppercorns, crushed
1/2 teaspoon salt (optional)
12 ounces dry curd cottage cheese (less than 1/2% fat)
1 1/2 ounces feta cheese (made with part skim milk if available)

6 ounces freshly grated part skim milk Parmesan cheese
1/4 to 1/2 cup skim milk, heated to boiling
2 1/2 (14-ounce) cans Hunt's stewed tomatoes (no added salt)
3 tablespoons tomato paste
10 ounces spinach, washed, stalks removed, coarsely shredded
8 ounces no-boil lasagna noodles
1 cup (packed) fresh basil leaves (or 1/2 cup frozen or 1 tablespoon dry), washed and coarsely chopped

☐ Sort, wash then chop the dry mushrooms and place in the dry vermouth to soak until soft, set aside (this usually takes 20 to 30 minutes). Oil baking dish with vegetable cooking spray and set aside. (This fits best into 13x9x3-inch baking dish).

☐ Heat the olive oil in a large sauté pan and add the shallots, cook over moderate heat until transparent. Add the garlic, allow to cook a few minutes longer then add the fresh mushrooms. Once the mushrooms exude some of their liquid, turn up the heat and cook until they are wilted. Add the vermouth soaked dry mushrooms to the sauté pan. Continue to cook until the liquid reduces by 1/4. Stir in the green peppercorns and salt if desired. To prepare the cheese sauce, combine the cottage cheese, feta, Parmesan (reserve 1/4 cup to sprinkle on top) and heated skim milk in a blender or food processor and purée until smooth.

☐ Combine the tomatoes and tomato paste in blender or food processor. Process until smooth. In bottom of baking dish, spread a thin layer of tomato sauce and drizzle with a small amount of the cheese mixture. Then begin layering the ingredients sparsely in the following order—pasta, spinach, mushrooms, basil, tomato sauce and cheese mixture. Follow this order until you have used up all the ingredients, reserving enough cheese to cover final layer fairly evenly. You should get about five layers altogether. We have found that the lasagna is usually more attractive if you omit spinach in the final layer. Lightly oil 3-inch wide strips of foil and tuck them loosely around the edges of the dish to avoid getting dried out crusty edges.

☐ Sprinkle with reserved Parmesan and bake, loosely covered with oiled foil, in the center of a preheated 400° F. oven for 30 minutes, remove the cover and bake for an additional 15 minutes or until bubbly.

☐ Makes 8 servings.

Per serving: Calories 317, Protein 22 g., Fat 8 g., 23% fat, (12% saturated fat), Carbohydrates 40 g., Dietary fiber 5 g., Cholesterol 22 mg., Sodium 598 mg., Calcium 383 mg., Iron 4.2 mg.
Exchanges: meat 2; bread 1 1/2; vegetable 3

KIDS COOKOUT

Corn on the Cob on the Grill
page 108

Easy Potato Wedges
page 102

Fruit Salad
page 107

Baked Beans with Apples and Leeks
page 106

Turkey Burgers with Whole Grain
and Oat Bran Rolls
pages 77 and 63

Strawberry Blender Shake
page 33

Raisin-Oatmeal Cookies
page 115

Per serving for complete menu:
Calories 980, Protein 52 g.,
Fat 15 gm. (total = 14% saturated = *%),
Carbohydrates 173 g., Dietary fiber 27 g.,
Cholesterol 77 mg., Sodium 644 mg.,
Calcium 443 mg., Iron 8.8 mg.
*Data not available at this time.

RAISIN-OATMEAL COOKIES

Vegetable cooking spray
2 medium carrots (1½ cups)
1 cup golden raisins
½ cup dark brown sugar
2 tablespoons canola oil
2 tablespoons molasses

2 cups old-fashioned oatmeal
*1 cup barley flour
1 teaspoon baking soda
1 teaspoon cinnamon
½ cup dark raisins

☐ Preheat oven to 375° F. Lightly spray 2 large cookie sheets with vegetable spray. Purée carrots in a food processor or blender. Add the next 4 ingredients, purée again. Combine the remaining ingredients, fold into the carrot mixture. Drop by the spoonful onto prepared cookie sheets. Bake for 10 to 12 minutes or until golden. Remove from cookie sheets onto racks to cool. Store in an airtight container.

☐ Makes 3 dozen cookies.

☐ NOTE: *Barley flour is available in the *health food* section of supermarkets and in co-ops.

Per 1 cookie serving: Calories 63, Protein 1 g., Fat 1 g., 14% fat (2% saturated fat),
Carbohydrates 13 g., Dietary fiber 1 g., Cholesterol 0 mg., Sodium 5 mg.,
Calcium 18 mg., Iron 0.7 mg.
Exchanges: bread ½; fruit ½ (Not recommended for diabetics)

DINNER PARTY FOR EIGHT

Spicy Autumn Harvest Soup
page 51

Individual Fruit Salads
with Lime-Ginger Dressing
page 50

Medallions of Norwegian
Salmon or Swordfish
page 116

Crusty Whole Wheat
Braids (2 Slices)
page 61

Fruity Raspberry Sorbet
in Meringue Shells
page 128

Per serving for complete menu:
Calories 864, Protein 39 g.,
Fat 29 g. (total = 30% saturated = 4%),
Carbohydrates 113 g., Dietary fiber 12 g.,
Cholesterol 71 mg., Sodium 296 mg.,
Calcium 189 mg., Iron 4.4 mg.

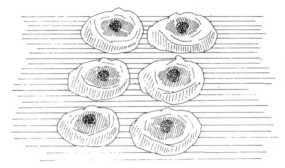

MEDALLIONS OF NORWEGIAN SALMON OR SWORDFISH

2 tablespoons fruity olive oil
  divided
1 pound Norwegian salmon
  (substitute swordfish or Mako
  shark) cut into 1/4-inch slices
2 tablespoons all-purpose flour
Salt and freshly ground pepper to
  taste
Zest of 1/2 lemon
Juice of 1/2 lemon

1 medium shallot, peeled and finely
  chopped
1/2 pound mushrooms, thinly sliced
1/2 cup Chardonnay (white wine)
1 tablespoon fresh dill, chopped
  finely (lemon thyme may be used)
1 teaspoon Dijon-style mustard
1 1/2 ounces fromage blanc (low-fat
  soft cheese or Yogurt Cheese)

☐ Preheat 2 teaspoons of the olive oil in a medium-sized sauté pan over moderately high heat. Lightly dust the fish with the flour, salt and pepper and sauté small batches for about 20 seconds per side adding more oil as necessary. Remove to a preheated platter and sprinkle with the lemon juice and zest. Cover and keep warm.

☐ Add 2 teaspoons olive oil to the sauté pan, turn down the heat and sauté the shallots until transparent, about 1 minute stirring. Add the mushrooms and turn up the heat as soon as they begin to give off their moisture, cook for 3 minutes stirring constantly. Add the Chardonnay and bring to a full boil to reduce the liquid volume by at least one-half. Stir in the dill, mustard and fromage blanc and pour over the fish. Serve immediately garnished with a sprig of the dill.

☐ Makes 4 servings.

Per serving: Calories 319, Protein 28 g., Fat 17 g., 48% fat, (8% saturated fat), Carbohydrates 9 g., Dietary fiber 2 g., Cholesterol 71 mg., Sodium 75 mg., Calcium 31 mg., Iron 1.8 mg.
Exchanges: lean meat 4; vegetables 1; fat 1

Shallots These little culinary gems are the best possible combination of the onion and garlic, somewhat on the delicate side. They are related to them both. You will notice we make liberal use of these throughout the book. They are best lightly sautèed or marinated or their flavor will overwhelm. Choose firm plump cloves.

FORMAL DINNER SETTING

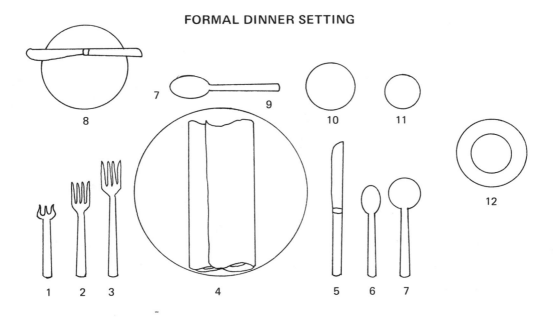

Tableware used first is placed fartherest from plate.

1. Cocktail fork
2. Salad fork
3. Dinner fork
4. Dinner plate
5. Dinner knife
6. Teaspoon
7. Soup spoon
8. Bread and butter plate
   with butter knife
9. Dessert spoon
10. Water glass
11. Wine glass
12. Cup and saucer

ENTERTAINING ON THE PATIO

Blueberry Blender Shake
page 33

A Variety of Vegetables on the Grill
page 101

Grilled Butterflied Leg of Lamb
page 95

Broccoli Mushroom Bulgur Salad
page 48

Honey Whole Wheat Bread
with Walnuts

page 62

Festive Cranberry Conserve

page 118

Hazelnut Pavlova with Hazelnut
Custard Filling
page 132

Per serving for complete menu:
Calories 1032, Protein 49 g.,
Fat 32 g. (total = 28% saturated = *%),
Carbohydrates 137 g., Dietary fiber 15 g.,
Cholesterol 85 mg., Sodium 642 mg.,
Calcium 490 mg., Iron 10 mg.
*Data not available at this time.

FESTIVE CRANBERRY CONSERVE

Excellent with turkey for the holidays. It is also a wonderful accompaniment to lamb
and curried dishes. Will last for three months refrigerated or a year in your freezer.
Great for gift giving during the holiday season.

2 pounds cranberries, fresh or
frozen
2 pears, peeled, cored, diced
3 tart apples, peeled, cored and
sliced
2 cups golden raisins

2 cups brown sugar
2 tablespoons orange peel zest
1 cup orange juice
2 teaspoons ground cinnamon
1/4 teaspoon nutmeg
1/2 cup orange liqueur (optional)

☐ Combine all ingredients except liqueur in a large stainless steel pot. Bring to a boil,
lower the heat to medium and cook, covered, until the mixture thickens. This will take
at least an hour. Add the liqueur and chill for 4 hours or overnight.

☐ Makes 8 cups. (photo page 109)

Per 2 tablespoon serving: Calories 63, Protein trace, Fat trace, Carbohydrates 15 g.,
Dietary fiber 1 g., Cholesterol 0 mg., Sodium 3 mg., Calcium 12 mg., Iron 0.4 mg.
Exchanges: fruit 1 (Not recommended for diabetics)

DESSERTS

Michigan Black Bean Soup
page 53

Chef Bill's Raspberry Chicken with Poached Pears
page 67

Easy Rice Pilaf
page 107

Quick Zucchini Stir-Fry
page 104

Honey Whole Wheat Bread
with Walnuts
page 62

Raspberry Chiffon Cheesecake
page 122

Per serving for complete menu: Calories 981, Protein 58 g., Fat 19 g. (total = 17% saturated= 2%), Carbohydrates 154 g., Dietary fiber 25 g., Cholesterol 69 mg., Sodium 872 mg., Calcium 491 mg., Iron 10.4 mg.

This chapter includes something for everyone and every occasion. You will notice there are many "do ahead" tips, and also simple down home recipes. When testing these recipes with the MedSport staff, we received rave reviews and comments such as: "This is so deliciously decadent I must have really blown my diet." This comment refers to the Raspberry Chiffon Cheesecake, on page 122, which has 255 calories per serving and is less than 10% fat! Try it for yourselves.

Photograph: Blackberry Sorbet, Raspberry Chiffon Cheesecake, Marge Monaghan's Fabulous Microwave Fudge, Almond Apricot Delights, Cocoa Date Truffles, Raisin-Oatmeal Cookies, pages 138, 122, 140, 141, 142 and 115

CHERRY SWIRL CHEESECAKE

The Crust:
2 ounces Sunshine brand
  "Grahamy Bears" crackers
1/2 tablespoon acceptable margarine

1 teaspoon water
Vegetable cooking spray

The Filling:
*32 ounces vanilla low-fat yogurt,
  drained overnight (see page 34)
4 teaspoons cornstarch
1 tablespoon Kirsch or other berry
  liqueur, (optional)

1/2 teaspoon vanilla
3 egg whites
1/4 cup cherry preserves, puréed
1 to 2 teaspoons cherry preserves,
  strained, (optional)

The Topping:
3/4 cup drained plain nonfat
  yogurt (drain this to sour cream
  consistency, yields 1/2 cup)

☐ Preheat oven to 375° F. Combine the crust ingredients and press them into the base of the greased cake pan.

☐ Bake in preheated oven for 5 minutes; cool on rack.

☐ In a bowl, combine the drained yogurt, cornstarch, liqueur and vanilla and stir until smooth. Do not whip this too vigorously or you will break down the structure of the yogurt.

☐ In another bowl, whip the egg whites until fluffy, but not stiff (about 3 minutes), fold egg whites into the yogurt mixture.

☐ Pour half of the yogurt mixture into the cake pan, spread the preserves on top, then pour in the remaining yogurt mixture. Cut through the mixture with a knife to swirl the preserves. Bake in a preheated 325° F. oven for 50 to 55 minutes, or until it springs back when lightly pressed with the fingers. Cool on a rack.

☐ When completely cool, spread with the plain yogurt sour cream, make marks with the tines of a fork. Melt strained preserves to liquid consistency and spread on top for optional glaze. Garnish with fresh fruit if desired.

☐ Makes 8 servings.

☐ NOTE: *If using nonfat plain yogurt for the filling, increase the vanilla to 1 teaspoon and add 3 tablespoons sugar to the egg whites.

Variation: Try other flavors of preserves such as raspberry, strawberry, blueberry or apricot.

Per serving: Calories 201, Protein 8 g., Fat 4 g., 18% fat (* saturated fat),
  Carbohydrates 35 g., Dietary fiber 1 g., Cholesterol trace, Sodium 155 mg.,
  Calcium 247 mg., Iron 0.3 mg. *Data not available at this time.
Exchanges: bread 1/2; fruit 1/2; skim milk 11/2; fat 1 (Not recommended for diabetics)

RASPBERRY CHIFFON CHEESECAKE

Crust

6 ounces low-fat graham crackers, ground	1 teaspoon ground cinnamon
1/3 cup honey	2 egg whites

☐ Preheat oven to 350° F. Combine graham cracker crumbs, honey and cinnamon. Beat egg whites until stiff and fold in crumb mixture. Press mixture into the bottom of a 10-inch removable bottom cake pan which you have first lined with lightly oiled aluminum foil. Bake at 350° F. for 25 minutes. Cool completely, remove crust and peel off foil then return the crust to the pan.

Filling

1 tablespoon plus 1 teaspoon gelatin granules	3/4 cup sugar, divided
1/4 cup water	1 teaspoon vanilla
5 tablespoons seedless raspberry preserves, divided	1/4 cup evaporated skim milk
12 ounces dry curd cottage cheese	2 tablespoons water
2 cups Yogurt Cheese (made from 1 quart nonfat yogurt, page 34)	3 egg whites
	1 fresh kiwifruit, sliced
	1 pint fresh raspberries

☐ Sprinkle gelatin over 1/4 cup water in a small saucepan. Set aside. Combine 3 tablespoons of the raspberry preserves with cottage cheese, yogurt cheese, 1/3 cup sugar and vanilla in the bowl of a food processor or blender. Process until smooth.

☐ Cook gelatin over low heat, stirring occasionally until gelatin dissolves. Stir in evaporated skim milk. With food processor or blender running, slowly add gelatin mixture to cottage cheese mixture. Transfer to a large mixing bowl. Combine remaining sugar and 2 tablespoons water in a small saucepan, stir to dissolve. Bring to a boil *without stirring* and continue to boil until the mixture reaches *soft-ball* stage (when a teaspoon of hot syrup is dropped into iced water it can be shaped into a ball with fingertips).

☐ Beat egg whites until stiff peaks form. Gradually pour hot syrup in a thin stream over egg whites, beating constantly. Beat at medium speed for 10 minutes, then at high speed for an additional 1 minute. Beat in 1 cup of cottage cheese mixture on low speed. Fold egg white mixture into remaining cottage cheese mixture. Pour into prepared crust and refrigerate for at least 4 hours. To remove cheesecake from pan, run a hot knife around the edge of the pan then remove sides. Warm the remaining raspberry preserves and whisk with a fork to get a soft consistency, pour over the top of the cake, smooth with spatula to cover entire surface. Garnish with the fresh raspberries and sliced kiwi (see photo page 119).

☐ Makes 12 servings.

Per serving: Calories 255, Protein 13 g., Fat 2 g., 7% fat (* saturated fat), Carbohydrates 48 g., Dietary fiber 2 g., Cholesterol 3 mg., Sodium 185 mg., Calcium 186 mg., Iron 1 mg. *Data not available at this time.
Exchanges: lean meat 1; bread 1/2; fruit 2; skim milk 1/2 (Not recommended for diabetics)

CHOCOLATE SWIRL AMARETTO CHEESECAKE

The chocolate syrup recipe stands alone as a sauce for fresh fruit or frozen yogurt.

Crust

3 ounces chocolate flavored
graham crackers (Chocolate Teddy
Grahams)
1 tablespoon cocoa (Swiss or Dutch
processed)

1/4 cup lightly toasted almonds,
ground
2 tablespoons amaretto liqueur
Vegetable cooking spray

☐ Preheat oven to 450° F. Combine all ingredients in food processor and grind to a coarse powder consistency. Press into a lightly oiled 7-inch springform cake pan and bake for 8 to 10 minutes. Cool on a rack.

Chocolate Syrup

1 tablespoon plus 2 teaspoons cocoa
(Swiss or Dutch processed)

3 tablespoons dark brown sugar
2 tablespoons evaporated skim milk

☐ Combine all ingredients and heat in a saucepan or microwave to boiling, stir to incorporate ingredients, set aside.

Filling

2 cups yogurt cheese* (made from
1 quart of nonfat yogurt)
2 tablespoons amaretto liqueur
4 teaspoons cornstarch

1 teaspoon pure vanilla extract
4 egg whites
1/4 cup plus 1 tablespoon sugar

☐ **Drain the yogurt the night before!**

☐ Preheat oven to 325° F. In a medium-sized bowl, combine the amaretto, cornstarch and vanilla, mix until smooth. Fold in the yogurt cheese. Whisk the egg whites until frothy then gradually add the sugar, continue to beat until the mixture begins to stiffen. Fold into the yogurt cheese mixture.

☐ Spread 1/2 of the batter into the cake pan, spoon 1/2 of the chocolate syrup at intervals over the batter then swirl with a spatula. Repeat with remaining batter and syrup to create a design on the final layer. Bake for 55 to 65 minutes, or until batter feels slightly springy to the touch.

☐ Makes 6 servings.

☐ NOTE: The crust and chocolate syrup may be made a day ahead. *To make yogurt cheese, drain the yogurt through cheesecloth or a yogurt funnel for 4 hours or overnight to remove the whey.

Per serving: Calories 274, Protein 14 g., Fat 6 g., 19% fat (2% saturated fat),
Carbohydrates 45 g., Dietary fiber 1, Cholesterol 3 mg., Sodium 270 mg.,
Calcium 348 mg., Iron 1 mg.
Exchanges: skim milk 1 1/2; bread 1/2; fruit 1 1/2; fat 1 (Not recommended for diabetics)

CHOCOLATE MARZIPAN TART WITH FRESH FRUIT TOPPING

Crust:

1/2 cup almonds
1/2 cup oatbran
3/4 cup whole wheat pastry flour (or
  1/2 whole wheat and 1/2 all-purpose)
2 tablespoons brown sugar

4 tablespoons acceptable margarine,
  well chilled and cut into cubes
2 tablespoons iced water
Vegetable cooking spray

☐ Finely grind the almonds in food processor or blender. Add oatbran, pastry flour and brown sugar; pulse to combine. With the machine running, drop in margarine and process until well mixed. Also with the machine running, add enough iced water to hold the dough together. Avoid over processing at this step or the dough will become tough. Allow dough to rest, refrigerated, for 30 minutes (if time permits), then roll out on a cool surface to fit a lightly oiled 10-inch tart pan (a tart pan with removable bottom works best). Refrigerate for at least 30 minutes before baking to avoid shrinking.

Filling:

6 ounces almond paste
1/2 cup brown sugar
4 egg whites

2 tablespoons good quality cocoa
  (Giradelli or Droste)

Glaze:

4 tablespoons apple jelly

4 teaspoons cognac

Garnish:

1 pint fresh berries and 2 kiwis

☐ Process the almond paste to break it up, add the brown sugar, egg whites and cocoa, continue to process for a couple of minutes until the texture is smooth. Combine the apple jelly and cognac and heat until the jelly dissolves.

Assembly

☐ Preheat oven to 400° F. Line crust with waxed paper and weight it with uncooked rice, this will prevent shrinking. Bake weighted crust for 10 minutes, remove paper and rice and return crust to oven for an additional 5 to 10 minutes or until light golden. To avoid burning the edges of the crust, cut the center out of a 12-inch foil pizza pan (leaving a 3-inch border) and set this on top of crust to shield the edges. Cool on a rack, then lightly brush with some of the glaze. (This helps waterproof the crust for a crunchy texture.)

☐ Spread marzipan mixture over cooled crust and bake in middle of a preheated oven for 20 to 30 minutes or until firm to the touch. When cool, glaze with remaining apple jelly and cognac mixture. Use the pizza pan shield to prevent the tart edges from burning. This piece of equipment can be washed and used many times. Oil it lightly to prevent it sticking to the tart filling. When cool, garnish with fresh fruit such as raspberries, kiwi or strawberries or a combination of all three. Reheat glaze and brush it over fruit.

☐ Makes 10 servings.

Per serving: Calories 264, Protein 8 g., Fat 11 g., 38% fat (4% saturated fat),
  Carbohydrates 40 g., Dietary fiber 7 g., Cholesterol 40 mg., Sodium 38 mg.,
  Calcium 86 mg., Iron 2.2 mg.
Exchanges: fruit 1 1/2; bread 1; fat 3

SPICY CRANBERRY-PEAR CRISP

Filling:

4 medium ripe pears such as
   Scarlet Bartlets (you can
   substitute apples)
2¹/₂ cups fresh or frozen cranberries
³/₄ cup brown sugar

¹/₄ cup barley flour (or oat bran)
¹/₄ teaspoon ground allspice*
¹/₄ teaspoon ground cardamom*
2 tablespoons frozen concentrated
   orange juice

Topping:

¹/₄ cup brown sugar
¹/₂ cup oat bran
¹/₂ cup oatmeal

1 tablespoon canola oil
¹/₄ cup sliced almonds

- Preheat oven to 400° F. and lightly oil (using one of the vegetable cooking sprays) a 12-inch diameter pie dish. Wash, core and thinly slice the pears. Wash and sort the cranberries. Combine fruit with the rest of the filling ingredients, mixing well, then arrange in the baking dish. Combine the topping ingredients and sprinkle evenly over the fruit. Bake in the middle of the preheated oven for 35 to 45 minutes or until lightly browned on top and the fruit is bubbly. If the top begins to brown too soon, tent with foil or parchment.

- Best served slightly warm or at room temperature.

- Makes 11 servings.

- NOTE: *Buy whole spices and grind in a mortar and pestle just before using for optimum flavor.

- Vary the fruit according to what's in season; dried cranberries may be substituted for fresh ones, increase the orange juice to ¹/₃ cup.

Per serving: Calories 186, Protein 2 g., Fat 3 g., 15% fat (1% saturated fat),
   Carbohydrates 39 g., Dietary fiber 3 g., Cholesterol 0 mg., Sodium 7 mg.,
   Calcium 34 mg., Iron 1 mg.
Exchanges: bread ¹/₂; fruit 2; fat ¹/₂ (Not recommended for diabetics)

SUMMER STRAWBERRIES WITH RASPBERRY SAUCE

1 quart of fresh strawberries
1 tablespoon raspberry liqueur
(optional)
10 ounces fresh or frozen
raspberries

1 tablespoon powdered sugar
(optional)

☐ Slice the strawberries and toss with the liqueur if desired. Reserve 8 smaller berries for garnish. Purée the raspberries and press through a sieve to remove seeds. Fold in the optional powdered sugar. Serve the strawberries in 8 individual bowls. Spoon raspberry sauce over each serving and garnish with a reserved strawberry.

☐ Makes 8 servings.

☐ NOTE: Try this in meringue shells for a variation (page 130).

Per serving: Calories 50, Protein 1 g., Fat trace, Carbohydrates 11 g., Dietary fiber 3 g., Cholesterol 0 mg., Sodium 1 mg., Calcium 19 mg., Iron 0.5 mg.
Exchanges: fruit 1

RICE PUDDING

1 cup short grain brown rice
(we like Lundberg)
1 cup short or medium grain white
rice
9 cups boiling water, keep 1 cup in
reserve
3 egg whites

1 cup packed brown sugar
1 cup golden raisins
3 cups skim milk powder (instant)
1/2 teaspoon cardamom
2 teaspoons pure vanilla extract
1/2 teaspoon nutmeg, freshly grated
if possible

☐ Preheat oven to 350° F. Combine rice and 8 cups of boiling water. Return to a boil, and cook on medium-low boil for 30 to 40 minutes, partially covered, until rice is tender. The consistency of this mixture should still be quite liquid. Meanwhile, whip egg whites and sugar together to form soft peaks. Add raisins plus reserved hot water. Fold in dry milk powder, cardamom and vanilla. Combine rice (including all of its liquid) with the egg white mixture (off the heat to prevent curdling). Ladle into a 13x9x2-inch baking dish. Sprinkle evenly with nutmeg and place in a water bath* in a preheated oven to bake until set. This will take between 1 hour and 1 hour and 15 minutes. Best served at room temperature.

☐ Makes 24 servings.

☐ NOTE: If pudding appears a little dry as it begins to cool, pour 1/2 to 1 cup of boiling water evenly over top. This will completely absorb and rehydrate the pudding. *To assemble a water bath, place a pan large enough to hold your baking dish in the oven and fill with sufficient water to come 1/2 way up the sides of the baking dish. You may need to replenish the water with more **boiling** water as it evaporates.

Variations: Try soaking the raisins in ¹/₂ cup rum and reducing the reserved water by ¹/₂ cup. Vary the fruit: Michigan dried cherries, apricots or dates are excellent alternatives. For a less fibrous texture use all arborio rice (available at specialty food stores); however you will not be getting all the fiber as you do using brown rice. Omit the sugar, and pour ¹/₂ cup maple syrup over the pudding after it has been baking for 10 minutes, pierce with a fork at regular intervals to help the syrup absorb evenly.

Per serving: Calories 122, Protein 4 g., Fat trace, 2% fat (1% saturated fat), Carbohydrates 26 g., Dietary fiber 1 g., Cholesterol 2 mg., Sodium 57 mg., Calcium 119 mg., Iron 1 mg.
Exchanges: fruit ¹/₂; bread 1; skim milk ¹/₂ (Not recommended for diabetics)

LIGHT AND REFRESHING BLUEBERRY-PEACH CRISP

Filling:

6 ripe peaches (if underripe you
  may wish to increase the sugar)
1 pint of blueberries

¹/₄ cup brown sugar
1 teaspoon cinnamon
Vegetable cooking spray

Topping:

¹/₄ cup brown sugar
¹/₂ cup oat bran

1 tablespoon canola oil
¹/₄ cup chopped pecans or almonds

☐ Preheat oven to 400° F.

☐ Peel and slice the peaches, sort the blueberries. Combine fruit with brown sugar and cinnamon, then arrange in a baking dish (a 12-inch diameter pie dish works well), coated with vegetable cooking spray.

☐ Combine the topping ingredients and sprinkle evenly over the fruit. Bake in the middle of a preheated oven for 30 minutes or until lightly brown on top and the fruit is bubbly. Do not overcook.

☐ Best served at room temperature.

☐ Makes 8 servings. (photo on Cover)

☐ NOTE: For an interesting variation, combine ¹/₂ pound diced rhubarb, 2 large tart apples (peeled, cored and sliced), ³/₄ cup brown sugar and 1 teaspoon cinnamon. Place in a baking dish coated with vegetable cooking spray. Combine ¹/₂ cup brown sugar, ²/₃ cup oat bran, 1 tablespoon canola oil and ¹/₄ cup chopped pecans or almonds. Sprinkle over fruit. Bake at 400° F. for 30 minutes or until light brown and bubbly.

Per serving: Calories 163, Protein 2 g., Fat 5 g., 28% fat (2% saturated fat), Carbohydrates 30 g., Dietary fiber 4 g., Cholesterol 0 mg., Sodium 7 mg., Calcium 23 mg., Iron 0.8 mg.
Exchanges: fruit 2; fat 1 (Not recommended for diabetics)

FRUITY RASPBERRY SORBET IN MERINGUE SHELLS

12 ounces raspberries, frozen
1/2 cup seedless raspberry preserves

1/2 cup frozen concentrated apple juice

☐ Place raspberries in a food processor fitted with the steel blade and process until granular in appearance.

☐ Add the raspberry preserves and apple juice and blend until smooth.

☐ Press the mixture through a sieve to remove the seeds, then freeze in sealed container.

☐ Purée again to lighten the sorbet 3 to 4 hours before serving.

☐ Makes 10 servings.

Per serving: (sorbet only) Calories 68, Protein trace, Fat trace, Carbohydrates 17 g.,
Dietary fiber 1 g., Cholesterol 0 mg., Sodium 2 mg., Calcium 11 mg., Iron 0.4 mg.
Exchanges: fruit 1

Meringue Shells
2 egg whites
3/4 cup sugar
1 tablespoon boiling water

1 teaspoon vanilla
1 teaspoon cornstarch
1/4 cup sugar

☐ Preheat oven to 300° F. Combine first 5 ingredients in a large mixing bowl and beat on high speed until the sugar dissolves.

☐ Gradually add enough of the remaining sugar to form a stiff mixture.

☐ Pipe onto waxed paper in the shape of cups, 2 inches in diameter and bake in a preheated oven for 30 minutes. Turn down the heat to 200° F. and bake an additional 20 minutes. Cool completely in oven with the door closed.

☐ To serve scoop a generous portion of sorbet into each meringue shell and garnish with mint leaves and some fresh raspberries if available.

☐ Makes 10 servings.

☐ NOTE: Meringues will keep in an airtight container for 10 days.

Per serving: (meringue shell): Calories 81, Protein 1 g., Fat trace., Carbohydrates 20 g.,
Dietary fiber 0 g., Cholesterol 0 mg., Sodium 10 mg., Calcium 1 mg., Iron trace.
Exchanges: fruit 1 1/2 (Not recommended for diabetics)

Per serving: (sorbet and meringue): Calories 149, Protein 1 g., Fat trace,
Carbohydrates 37 g., Dietary fiber 1g., Cholesterol 0 mg., Sodium 12 mg.,
Calcium 12 mg., Iron 0.4 mg.
Exchanges: fruit 2 1/2 (Not recommended for diabetics)

QUICK 'N EASY RASPBERRY SORBET SURPRISE

1 recipe Fruity Raspberry Sorbet
(see page 128) or 1/2 quart of your
favorite brand
1 1/2 cups lite tofutti (vanilla almond
bark is great for this or vanilla
chocolate swirl frozen low-fat
yogurt)

1 pint fresh raspberries and or
mint for garnish (optional)

☐ Soften the frozen sorbet, then press it around the outside edge of an 8-cup mold. If
the sorbet is sliding into the middle, press an empty plastic container into the middle
to keep the space. Cover and return to the freezer until firm.

☐ Whip the tofutti or frozen yogurt to soften it, remove the space retainer from the
center of the sorbet and fill it with the softened tofutti or frozen yogurt. Return to the
freezer until firm. Unmold and serve garnished with the fresh raspberries and mint
leaves.

☐ Makes 8 servings.

Per serving: Calories 130, Protein 2 g., Fat 1 g., 7% fat (trace saturated fat),
  Carbohydrates 30 g., Dietary fiber 4 g., Cholesterol 3 mg., Sodium 15 mg.,
  Calcium 54 mg., Iron 0.5 mg.
Exchanges: fruit 1 1/2; skim milk 1/2

FROZEN YOGURT FRUIT PIE

Crust:

2 ounces Sunshine brand "Grahamy Bears" crackers

1 rounded tablespoon ground pecans, hazelnuts or walnuts (lightly toasted)

1/2 tablespoon acceptable margarine

Vegetable oil cooking spray

Filling:

1 1/2 quarts nonfat frozen vanilla yogurt

2 cups fresh fruit (strawberry, kiwifruit, blueberries, peaches, cherries, raspberries or pineapple)

Fresh mint for garnish (optional)

☐ Preheat the oven to 400° F.

☐ In the food processor crumble the cookies and mix them with the pecans and margarine. Lightly coat 8-inch pie dish with cooking spray.

☐ Press the crumbled cookie mixture into the base of a lightly sprayed 8-inch pie dish (it will only go about 1/2 way up the sides). Bake in preheated oven for 5 minutes; cool on wire rack.

☐ Whip the frozen yogurt into a workable consistency, you can do this by hand, then spread it into the pie dish, mounding it in the middle to look like a pie. Return to the freezer to set until firm. Decorate with fresh fruit of choice. Garnish with fresh mint and serve at once.

☐ Makes 8 servings.

Per serving: Calories 220, Protein 5 g., Fat 6 g., 25% (* saturated fat),
Carbohydrates 38 g., Dietary fiber 2 g., Cholesterol 10 mg., Sodium 101 mg.,
Calcium 158 mg., Iron 0.4 mg. *Data not available at this time.
Exchanges: bread 1/2; fruit 1/2; skim milk 2; fat 1

POACHED PEARS WITH HAZELNUT CUSTARD

**6 firm ripe pears, peeled and cores
removed from the bottom with a
melon baller**
Juice of 1/2 lemon
2 cups water or white wine
1 teaspoon vanilla
**1/4 cup sugar, or more if the pears
are under ripe**

**1/2 recipe of Hazelnut Custard (see
page 132)**
**6 ounces strained raspberry
preserves**
**1 tablespoon berry liqueur (kirsch
or cassis)**
**Fresh raspberries and mint sprigs
(optional)**

☐ Sprinkle pears with lemon juice.

☐ Combine water, vanilla and sugar in a large saucepan. Place pears in saucepan and
cover. Bring to a boil, reduce heat and simmer for 20 minutes, turning pears after 10
minutes. Remove from liquid and cool completely.

☐ Spoon custard into cavity of each pear. Place pears on individual serving plates and
spoon any remaining custard around pears. Combine preserves and liqueur, spoon
over pears. Garnish with raspberries and mint sprigs.

☐ Makes 6 servings.

Per serving: Calories 286, Protein 5 g., Fat 2 g., 6% fat (1% saturated fat),
Carbohydrates 63 g., Dietary fiber 5 g., Cholesterol 1 mg., Sodium 35 mg.,
Calcium 108 mg., Iron 0.9 mg.
Exchanges: fruit 4; skim milk 1/2 (Not recommended for diabetics)

HAZELNUT PAVLOVA WITH HAZELNUT CUSTARD FILLING

Meringue Shell
- 4 egg whites
- 2 teaspoons cornstarch
- 1 teaspoon vinegar
- 1 teaspoon vanilla
- 4 tablespoons boiling water
- 1 cup plus 2 tablespoons sugar, divided
- 1/4 cup lightly roasted hazelnuts (do this in the toaster oven on darkest setting, when cool, rub them together in the palm of your hands to remove some of the brown skin), finely ground in food processor or blender

☐ Preheat the oven to 350° F.

☐ Prepare a heavy duty cookie sheet or pizza pan by greasing and lining it with waxed paper or parchment paper which you have cut into a large circle, grease the paper.

☐ Combine all of the ingredients, except 2 tablespoons sugar and the hazelnuts, in a large mixing bowl and beat until stiff (about 3 to 5 minutes), add the reserved sugar, beat an additional 30 seconds, then fold in the hazelnuts. Spoon out onto the paper-lined cookie sheet in little mounds to form a large circle, spread a small amount of the mixture into the center of the circle just to cover. Bake in the middle of a preheated 350° F. oven for 20 minutes, reduce heat to 300° F. for 20 minutes, then to 275° F. for 30 minutes. Turn off the oven and do not remove the shell until cool or for at least 20 minutes. Allow to cool completely before assembling.

☐ NOTE: You may have to adjust the oven temperature to accommodate your oven, if the meringue begins to brown, tent it with parchment or foil. Do not open the oven more than necessary as the constantly changing temperature may result in a flat meringue.

Hazelnut Custard:
- 1 teaspoon gelatin
- 2 tablespoons frangelica or amaretto liqueur (optional) or water
- 1/4 cup hazelnuts, roasted and finely ground (or almonds)
- 6 ounces skim milk cottage cheese
- 1/4 cup sugar
- 1 cup Yogurt Cheese (made from 2 cups nonfat plain yogurt) (see page 34)

☐ Sprinkle gelatin over liqueur in a small saucepan. Stir over low heat until dissolved. In the bowl of your food processor or blender, combine the hazelnuts, dissolved gelatin, cottage cheese and sugar. Blend until smooth, then with a few quick pulses, add the Yogurt Cheese. Mound the Hazelnut Custard into the center of the meringue shell and garnish with fresh fruit and sprigs of mint.

☐ Makes 10 servings.

Garnish: 1 pint of fresh berries such as strawberries, raspberries or blueberries, kiwifruit, passion fruit, sliced ripe peaches and mint leaves

---

Per serving: Calories 204, Protein 7 g., Fat 4 g., 18% fat (2% saturated fat), Carbohydrates 35 g., Dietary fiber 1 g., Cholesterol 2 mg., Sodium 57 mg., Calcium 110 mg., Iron 0.4 mg.
Exchanges: fruit 1 1/2; skim milk 1; fat 1 (Not recommended for diabetics)

IRISH BRAC TEA CAKE

1¹/₂ cups strong tea
2 cups brown sugar
2 cups golden raisins
2 cups dark raisins
3 egg whites
2 tablespoons sesame paste
  (available in health food section)

2¹/₂ cups whole wheat pastry flour
2 teaspoons baking powder
1¹/₂ teaspoons cinnamon
¹/₄ teaspoon ground cloves
¹/₂ teaspoon ground ginger
¹/₂ cup coarsely chopped walnuts

☐ Prepare loaf pans by spraying with vegetable cooking spray. Preheat oven to 325° F.

☐ Combine first 4 ingredients, stir well and allow to soak overnight. Whisk the egg whites, whisk in the sesame paste. Add this mixture to the raisins and tea. Set aside.

☐ Combine all the dry ingredients, then stir them into the raisin mixture until well combined. Stir in walnuts. Pour into loaf pans of choice and bake in a preheated oven for 30 minutes for mini-loaves or 1 hour and 20 to 30 minutes for regular-size loaf pans or until a toothpick inserted into the middle of the cake comes out clean. Invert onto cake racks to cool; wrap in aluminum foil to store.

☐ Makes 12 mini-loaves or 2 regular loaves.

Per mini loaf serving: Calories 442, Protein 7 g., Fat 5 g., 10% fat (1% saturated fat),
  Carbohydrates 99 g., Dietary fiber 7 g., Cholesterol 0 mg., Sodium 136 mg.,
  Calcium 108 mg., Iron 3.6 mg.
Exchanges: fruit 5; bread 1¹/₂; fat 1 (Not recommended for diabetics)

CHEATER'S BERRY COBBLER

2 pounds berries such as
blueberries, blackberries or
raspberries
2/3 cups brown sugar

1 teaspoon cinnamon
1 (15.4-ounce) package Pillsbury
nut bread mix

☐ Preheat oven to 400° F. Spray an 11x9x2-inch baking dish with vegetable cooking spray. Place berries in dish and sprinkle with sugar and cinnamon.

☐ Make up the nut bread mix according to the package directions except (a) substitute 2 egg whites instead of one whole egg (b) omit the 2 tablespoons oil.

☐ Pour the batter over the berries and bake in the preheated oven for 1 hour and 5 minutes or until a toothpick inserted into the center of the cobbler comes out clean.

☐ Makes 12 servings.

Per serving: Calories 237, Protein 3 g., Fat 3.5 g., 13% fat (* saturated fat),
Carbohydrates 48 g., Dietary fiber 3 g., Cholesterol 0 mg., Sodium 193 mg.,
Calcium 19 mg., Iron 0.6 mg. *Data not available at this time.
Exchanges: bread 1; fruit 2; fat 1 (Not recommended for diabetics)

STRAWBERRY RHUBARB CRUMBLE

Filling:
1 pound rhubarb, washed and cut
into 1-inch lengths
1 pound strawberries (1 quart),
cleaned, hulled and halved

1/4 cup tapioca
1 cup brown sugar
Vegetable cooking spray

Crumble:
1/2 cup oatmeal
1/4 cup oat bran
1/2 cup barley flour (available at
food cooperatives)
1/4 cup brown sugar

1 teaspoon baking powder
2 egg whites
1/4 cup chopped pecans (optional)
1 teaspoon cinnamon

☐ Preheat oven to 350° F.

☐ Combine all the filling ingredients in a large bowl and mix well. Pour into a 10-inch pie dish or a 8x10x2-inch baking dish coated with vegetable cooking spray.

☐ In the same large bowl, combine the crumble ingredients, except the pecans and cinnamon, and spread on top of the filling.

☐ Sprinkle with the pecans and cinnamon, and bake in a preheated oven for 45 minutes or until the filling is bubbly and the crumble is golden.

☐ Makes 8 servings.

Per serving: Calories 257, Protein 4 g., Fat 3 g., 11% fat (1% saturated fat), Carbohydrates 55 g., Dietary fiber 5 g., Cholesterol 0 mg., Sodium 79 mg., Calcium 121 mg., Iron 2 mg.
Exchanges: bread 1; fruit 2½; fat ½ (Not recommended for diabetics)

BAKED GOLDEN DELICIOUS APPLES WITH BLUEBERRY SAUCE

Best served warm or at room temperature, excellent as a dessert or to accompany whole grain pancakes for a hearty breakfast.

8 to 10 medium/large Golden Delicous apples, washed, cored and scored*
Vegetable cooking spray
1 (12-ounce) can concentrated fruit juice (apple, mixed berry, cran or blueberry)

1 pound fresh or frozen blueberries (you may substitute cherries or blackberries)
2 tablespoons **cornstarch or arrowroot, dissolved in 2 tablespoons water

☐ Preheat oven to 375° F. Place the apples into an 8½x11x2-inch baking dish sprayed with spray oil, and pour the frozen juice concentrate evenly over them.

☐ Distribute the berries around and into the cored apples.

☐ Bake in the middle of the preheated oven until the apples are tender when depressed, and the flesh of the apple puffs out where it was scored.

☐ Just before they're cooked, remove apples from the oven, stir in the dissolved cornstarch, and return them to the oven for a further 5 minutes, or until the sauce is bubbly.

☐ Makes 8 servings.

☐ *Make a shallow incision in the apple skin all the way around the apple.

☐ NOTE: **Because evaporation of juices during baking will vary, add the dissolved cornstarch gradually, stirring to disperse. Use only enough to achieve a thick syrup consistency.

Per serving: Calories 126, Protein 1 g., Fat 1 g., 7% fat (trace saturated fat), Carbohydrates 32 g., Dietary fiber 4 g., Cholesterol 0 mg., Sodium 3 mg., Calcium 15 mg., Iron 0.4 mg.
Exchanges: fruit 3

KATHY'S CARROT CAKE

This is a totally awesome cake without any eggs or dairy products!

3 cups finely shredded carrots
1¹/₂ cups dried fruit, prunes, dates
  or raisins
2¹/₄ cups water
1¹/₂ cups sugar
¹/₄ cup canola oil
1¹/₂ cups whole wheat pastry flour
  (or ¹/₂ whole wheat and ¹/₂
  all-purpose)
1 cup barley flour (or increase
  whole wheat pastry flour)
¹/₂ cup all-purpose flour (or cake
  flour)

2¹/₄ teaspoons baking soda
¹/₂ teaspoon allspice
¹/₄ teaspoon cloves
1 teaspoon nutmeg
1 teaspoon cinnamon
1¹/₂ teaspoons vanilla extract
¹/₂ cup confectioners' sugar
Lemon juice
1 pint fresh strawberries, optional
  garnish

☐ Preheat oven to 350° F. Combine the first 5 ingredients and bring to a boil, lower the heat and simmer for 10 minutes. **Cool completely*.** You can do this in your microwave (5 minutes 100%, then 10 minutes 50%). Cool.

☐ Stir the dry ingredients together, then pour the cooled liquid mixture into the dry ingredients. Add vanilla. Pour into a lightly oiled 13x9-inch baking dish.

☐ Bake in the middle of a preheated oven for 35 to 45 minutes or until a toothpick inserted comes out clean.

☐ Combine confectioners' sugar with enough lemon juice to achieve a honey consistency and brush over the cooled cake to glaze it.

☐ Garnish with fresh strawberries cut into halves (or slice if large) and placed around the edge of the cake.

☐ Makes 20 servings.

☐ NOTE: *To expedite cooling, place in a sink of cold water and replace the water when it becomes warm; may also be done the night before.

Variation: ¹/₃ cup of lightly roasted walnuts may be sprinkled on top of the glaze while it is still wet. (Not included in nutrient calculations.)

Per serving: Calories 198, Protein 3 g., Fat 3 g., 14% fat (2% saturated fat),
  Carbohydrates 42 g., Dietary fiber 4 g., Cholesterol 0 mg., Sodium 51 mg.,
  Calcium 42 mg., Iron 1 mg.
Exchanges: fruit 2; bread 1; fat ¹/₂ (Not recommended for diabetics)

BLUEBERRY APPLE COBBLER

4 golden delicious apples, peeled, cored and sliced
1 pound blueberries, washed and picked over (fresh or frozen)
1 1/4 cups brown sugar (divided into thirds)
1/2 teaspoon cinnamon

1 1/2 cups whole wheat pastry flour
1/2 cup oat bran
1 teaspoon baking powder
1 teaspoon cinnamon
3 egg whites
1/4 cup canola oil
3/4 cup skim milk

Topping:
2 tablespoons walnuts or pecans, finely chopped

1 tablespoon brown sugar

☐ Preheat oven to 400° F. Toss fruit in a large bowl with 1/3 of the sugar and 1/2 teaspoon cinnamon. Spread evenly into a 11x9x2 rectangular baking dish.

☐ Combine the remaining dry ingredients and mix well.

☐ Lightly beat the egg whites then combine with oil and milk; fold the liquid ingredients into the dry and pour over the fruit.

☐ Combine walnuts and 1 tablespoon brown sugar. Sprinkle over fruit and bake for 1 hour and 10 minutes or until a toothpick inserted into the center of the batter comes out clean. Best served warm.

☐ Makes 12 servings.

Variation: Use the batter for muffins, folding 1 1/2 cups blueberries into the batter. Reduce baking time to 35 minutes.

Per serving: Calories 258, Protein 4 g., Fat 6 g., 21% fat (2% saturated fat), Carbohydrates 49 g., Dietary fiber 4 g., Cholesterol 0 mg., Sodium 64 mg., Calcium 81 mg., Iron 1.4 mg.
Exchanges: fruit 2; bread 1; fat 1 (Not recommended for diabetics)

BLACKBERRY SORBET

1¹/₂ pounds blackberries (fresh or frozen)
1¹/₄ cups fresh apple cider (or 1 cup frozen concentrated apple juice)

1 tablespoon Cassis (optional)
3 tablespoons blackberry preserves, without seeds
¹/₂ cup plain nonfat yogurt

☐ Combine blackberries and cider in the food processor or blender and purée.

☐ Add the Cassis if desired and blackberry preserves, purée again to combine the ingredients.

☐ Press through a sieve or the colander and sieve attachment of your mixer to remove the seeds.

☐ Freeze in a covered container until almost solid. If the purée becomes too hard, leave it out of the refrigerator for an hour or so until soft enough to purée.

☐ Purée again the day you intend to serve and at this time, add the nonfat yogurt. This can be done 4 to 5 hours before serving. Serve plain or with Blackberry Applesauce.

☐ Makes 8 servings.

☐ NOTE: This recipe can be made a week ahead of time, except for the final purée and addition of the yogurt. (photo page 119)

> **Per serving:** Calories 96, Protein 1 g., Fat trace, Carbohydrates 22 g., Dietary fiber 5 g., Cholesterol trace, Sodium 12 mg., Calcium 57 mg., Iron 0.6 mg.
> **Exchanges:** fruit 1¹/₂

PIQUANT BLACKBERRY APPLESAUCE

2 tart apples (such as Granny Smith or Greenings), quartered and cored

2 cloves
¹/₂ cup apple cider
¹/₂ pound blackberries

☐ Combine apples, cloves and apple cider in a non-aluminum saucepan. Bring to a boil and simmer until the apples are tender. Remove the cloves and press through a sieve. Add the blackberries, stir thoroughly to combine and refrigerate until ready to serve. If you need to sweeten this sauce for your taste, add 1 to 2 tablespoons blackberry preserves.

☐ Makes 8 servings.

> **Per serving:** Calories 43, Protein trace, Fat trace, Carbohydrates 11 g., Dietary fiber 2 g., Cholesterol 0 mg., Sodium 1 mg., Calcium 14 mg., Iron 0.4 mg.
> **Exchanges:** fruit 1

PEAR RASPBERRY TART

Crust

1/2 cup almonds, ground
11/2 cups whole wheat flour pastry
1/2 cup oat bran
3 tablespoons brown sugar

1/2 cup acceptable unsalted
   margarine, well chilled and cut
   into small cubes
1 to 2 tablespoons iced water

Base

1/4 cup almonds, ground
2 tablespoons brown sugar
1/4 cup whole grain barley flour

4 small pears or 3 large ones
12 ounces raspberries, fresh or
   frozen

Glaze

1/2 cup red currant jelly

☐ Combine the first 4 crust ingredients; mix well. Cut in the margarine using a fork or pastry blender, or pulse several times in the food processor. Add enough of the iced water to hold the dough together. Refrigerate for 30 minutes.

☐ Combine all the ingredients for the base; set aside.

☐ Roll out the pastry on a lightly floured surface to fit a 10-inch tart pan. It will crumble easily. If you have a removable bottom tart pan, roll out the pastry directly onto it, having first lightly sprayed it with vegetable cooking spray. If pieces of pastry break off, just patch them back on again. Spread the base evenly over the pastry. Cover and refrigerate for at least 1/2 hour or overnight if more convenient.

☐ Peel pears and cut in half. Remove core. Cut vertically into 1/8-inch slices cutting from base toward stem, taking care not to completely cut through stem end.

☐ Preheat the oven to 400° F. Place pears on prepared crust. Spread slices apart slightly, taking care to retain the pear's shape. Bake for 30 minutes in the middle of the oven. Remove and place the raspberries around the pears. Return to the oven and bake an additional 30 minutes or until the crust is lightly golden. If the edges of the tart are cooking too quickly, cut the center out of a disposable pizza pan, leaving a 2-inch edge. Place this over the tart so that only the edges of the tart are covered. This marvelous piece of equipment can be used many times.

☐ Allow to cool then brush the fruit with the melted currant jelly. Serve at room temperature.

☐ Makes 12 servings.

☐ NOTE: If using fresh raspberries, cook tart completely and add when cooled.

Per serving: Calories 296, Protein 5 g., Fat 14 g., 42% fat (6% saturated fat),
  Carbohydrates 40 g., Dietary fiber 7 g., Cholesterol 0 mg., Sodium 94 mg.,
  Calcium 51 mg., Iron 1 mg.
Exchanges: bread 1; fruit 11/2; fat 3 (Not recommended for diabetics)

Cookies & Candies

MARGE MONAGHAN'S FABULOUS MICROWAVE FUDGE

3¹/₂ cups powdered sugar
¹/₂ cup cocoa
¹/₂ cup acceptable margarine

¹/₄ cup evaporated skim milk
1 teaspoon vanilla

☐ Stir powdered sugar and cocoa together in a 2-quart glass bowl. Place the stick of margarine on top and pour the evaporated skim milk over this without stirring. Microwave for 2 to 3 minutes on High to soften the margarine. Add the vanilla.

☐ Process 10 to 15 seconds in a food processor or whip smooth with a wooden spoon. Pour into a 8x8x2-inch pan which has been lined with plastic wrap. Refrigerate until set. Cut into 24 little squares. Serve chilled.

☐ Makes 24 servings. (photo page 119)

Per serving: Calories 100, Protein 1 g., Fat 4 g., 36% fat (6% saturated fat),
  Carbohydrates 16 g., Dietary fiber 0 g., Cholesterol 0 mg., Sodium 48 mg.,
  Calcium 12 mg., Iron 0.3 mg.
Exchanges: fruit 1; fat 1 (Not recommended for diabetics)

FRUITY CHOCOLATE AMARETTO MERINGUES

Parchment paper or baking paper
Spray lubricant
3 large egg whites
¹/₈ teaspoon cream of tartar
³/₄ cup granulated sugar
3 tablespoons unsweetened cocoa
  powder*
1 teaspoon amaretto liqueur
  (optional)

¹/₂ teaspoon almond extract
¹/₄ cup dried cranberries, cherries
  or apricots, cut into small dice
  (or your favorite dried fruit)
¹/₄ cup Maypo (or any instant)
  oatmeal hot cereal (uncooked)

☐ Preheat oven to 325°) F.

☐ Line 2 large cookie sheets with parchment paper and spray lightly with spray lubricant.

☐ Place the egg whites and cream of tartar in a large bowl and set the bowl over a saucepan of hot water. Whisk or beat the egg whites until well aerated and they hold their shape.

- Gradually add the sugar, in a thin stream, as you continue to beat the whites until they are thick and glossy. This will take about 3 to 4 minutes. Remove the bowl from the hot water. Add the cocoa, gradually, from a sieve or sifter, folding gently until well incorporated.

- Fold in the remaining ingredients.

- Drop by teaspoonful onto prepared cookie sheets.

- Bake in preheated oven for approximately 25 minutes, or until the outside is crisp and they become tinged with light golden color on their tips. If they begin to color too soon, turn the oven down to 300° F and tent with parchment paper. **Caution, do not overbake** as they will become bitter and very hard.

- Remove from the parchment paper onto wire racks to cool. Store in an airtight container. Will store for up to one week.

- Makes 40 meringues.

*Cocoa powder comes in a variety of qualities, for best flavor, use a superior quality such as Droste or Giradelli.

Per 2 cookie serving: Calories 39, Protein 1 g., Fat trace (5%), Carbohydrates 9 g., Sodium 19 mg., Cholesterol 0 mg., Calcium 1.7 mg., Iron .16 mg.
Exchanges: fruit 1/2

ALMOND APRICOT DELIGHTS

1 1/2 cups dried apricots, coarsely chopped
2 tablespoons cognac
1/2 cup almond paste
1/2 cup powdered sugar

2 teaspoons instant coffee
2 teaspoons cocoa
1/4 cup powdered sugar
1 teaspoon cocoa

- Combine the first 6 ingredients in food processor or blender and purée. Combine 1/4 cup powdered sugar and 1 teaspoon cocoa. Roll apricot mixture into marble-size balls and shake in the powdered sugar mixture. Store in an airtight container with the leftover powdered sugar mixture to prevent them from sticking. Best kept in the freezer.

- Makes 50 balls. (photo page 119)

- NOTE: A quick way to roll out the balls is to do it assembly line-fashion a dozen at a time by scooping out about a dozen little spoonfuls on waxed paper, then roll them one after the other and shake them all together.

Per serving (each) Calories 29, Protein 0 g., Fat 0.7 g., 21% fat (1% saturated fat), Carbohydrates 5 g., Dietary fiber 0 g., Cholesterol 0 mg., Sodium 3 mg., Calcium 9 mg., Iron 0.3 mg.
Exchanges: fruit 1/3; fat trace (Not recommended for diabetics)

COCOA DATE TRUFFLES

**2 cups pitted dates, coarsely
 chopped
2 tablespoons dark Jamaican rum
1/4 cup oat bran
1 tablespoon cocoa (we use Dutch**

**processed)
2 tablespoons powdered sugar
1/3 cup finely ground toasted
 almonds
1 teaspoon cocoa**

☐ In the bowl of a food processor or blender, purée the dates with the rum until smooth. Add the oat bran, 1 tablespoon cocoa and powdered sugar, and blend to combine. Place the almonds and cocoa in a paper bag. Shape a scant teaspoon of the mixture into tiny balls and shake in the almond/cocoa mixture in a paper bag to coat the truffles. You can shake several at a time. A quick way to roll out the balls is to do it assembly line-fashion a dozen at a time by scooping out about a dozen little spoonfuls onto waxed paper, then roll them one after another and shake them all together. Store in airtight containers in the refrigerator up to 2 weeks.

☐ Makes 4 dozen. (photo page 119)

Per 1 truffle serving: Calories 32, Protein 0.5 g., Fat 0.5 g., 14% fat (2% saturated fat),
  Carbohydrates 7 g., Dietary fiber 1 g., Cholesterol 0 mg., Sodium 3 mg.,
  Calcium 7 mg., Iron trace.
Exchanges: fruit 1/2

NO-BAKE HIGH FIBER ENERGY BARS

Kids of all ages love these bars!

**1/4 cup honey
6 cups miniature marshmallows
 (101/2-ounce package)**

**2 cups old-fashioned rolled oats
4 cups all-bran cereal
1 cup peanuts, dry roasted**

☐ In a large saucepan over moderate heat, combine the honey and marshmallows, stirring until dissolved.

☐ Add the rolled oats, all-bran and nuts. Stir until well coated.

☐ Press into a lightly greased 13x9x2-inch pan with wet hands (this reduces stickiness). Cut 7 times across and 4 times down, wiping the spatula with a damp paper towel between cuts to prevent it from sticking. Refrigerate.

☐ Makes 28 bars.

Per 1 bar serving: Calories 115, Protein 3 g., Fat 3 g., 23% fat (3% saturated fat),
  Carbohydrates 23 g., Dietary fiber 5 g., Cholesterol 0 mg., Sodium 152 mg.,
  Calcium 12 mg., Iron 2 mg.
Exchanges: bread 1; fruit 1/2; fat 1 (Not recommended for diabetics)

VENETIAN CORNMEAL COOKIES

1¹/₂ cups yellow cornmeal (whole grain)
1¹/₂ cups whole wheat pastry flour
¹/₂ cup sugar
1 teaspoon baking powder
1 cup (2 sticks) acceptable margarine

³/₄ cup lightly roasted pecans, coarsely chopped
³/₄ cup white (sultana) raisins
1 teaspoon grated lemon rind
3 egg whites
2 teaspoons pure vanilla extract

☐ Preheat oven to 350° F.

☐ Line two cookie sheets with waxed paper; set aside.

☐ Mix the cornmeal, flour, sugar and baking powder in a large bowl. Cut the margarine into ¹/₄-inch pieces and work into the dry ingredients until it resembles coarse meal (alternatively, you can divide this into two batches and combine the margarine in your food processor).

☐ Add the pecans and raisins; mix well.

☐ Combine the lemon rind, egg whites and vanilla in a small bowl; whisk well.

☐ Work the egg mixture into the dry ingredients with a fork and press into a ball. Cut into 4 pieces. On a lightly floured surface roll each piece into a 12x1-inch roll. (You can refrigerate the rolls up to 3 days at this stage.)

☐ Put two rolls on each cookie sheet and bake in the middle of the preheated oven for about 15 minutes or until they are golden and dry. Transfer roll to a work surface and cut diagonally with a serrated knife into 3/4-inch slices. Return cookies to the baking sheets and bake an additional 5 minutes, just until slightly dried. Transfer to a wire rack to cool.

☐ Makes 5 dozen.

☐ NOTE: These cookies will keep for up to 2 weeks in airtight containers lined with waxed paper. Handle with care, cookies crumble easily.

Per cookie serving: Calories 72, Protein 1 g., Fat 4 g., 50% fat (8% saturated fat), Carbohydrates 8 g., Dietary fiber 1 g., Cholesterol 0 mg., Sodium 45 mg., Calcium 5 mg., Iron trace.
Exchanges: bread ¹/₂; fat 1

PANTRY STAPLES

To help you get started into healthy eating habits, you may find it handy to have a well organized pantry. The following pantry list includes ingredients you need to have on hand to prepare recipes included in this book. If you are unable to find some of the items on these lists, check your grocer, many are happy to order items for you.

Canned low sodium-low fat chicken broth
Canned evaporated skim milk
Dried legumes–Black beans, navy beans, green and red lentils, split peas, red kidney beans, lima beans, blackeyed peas, Great Northern beans
Canned legumes-pinto, chic peas
Corn syrup
Canned stewed tomatoes-no added salt
Canola oil
Oatmeal
Brown rice
Wild rice
Dried pasta

Porcini, Cepes or Boletus dry wild mushrooms (for special occasions)
All purpose flour
White bread flour
Whole wheat bread flour
Cornmeal–whole grain
Rice flour
Barley flour
Dried apricots, raisins–black and golden, dates
Pitted prunes
Brown sugar
Granulated sugar
Baking powder
Baking soda
Whole Wheat Pastry Flour
Cocoa
Instant coffee
Confectioners' sugar

Honey
Quinoa
Cracked wheat
Sun dried tomatoes
Tomato paste
Dry yeast
Lasagna noodles (Del Verde No Boil, (save time and tastes good)
Vegetable cooking spray– plain and olive oil
Gelatin
Instant tapioca
Cornstarch
Arrowroot
Better than Bouillon vegetable, chicken and beef bases

QUICKIE MIXES FOR SHORTCUTS

Pillsbury Nut Bread
S&B Lemon Chicken Stir Fry (not recommended for low sodium diets)

Low Sodium vegetable soup mix

Carroll Shelby's Original Texas Brand Chili Mix

HERBS, SPICES AND SAUCES

Cinnamon
Whole nutmeg
Coriander
Cumin
Tumeric
Black peppercorns
Green peppercorns
Curry powder

Mustard seeds, black and white
Cayenne powder
Hungarian paprika–(keep refrigerated)
Sesame seeds
Chili powder
Cajun spices (low sodium)

Saffron threads
Ginger (ground for baking)
Cardamom
Allspice
Oregano
Marjoram
Bay leaf

Rosemary
Thyme
Lemon-Thyme
Mrs. Dash (lemon herb & original)
Angostura bitters

Clancy's Fancy hot sauce
Worcestershire sauce
Red wine vinegar
White wine vinegar
Raspberry wine vinegar
Cider vinegar

Sherry vinegar
Low-sodium soy sauce
Tamari sauce
Vanilla essence (pure)
Chocolate extract
Clam juice

ALCOHOL FOR COOKING

Dry Sherry
Dry Marsala (sweet will do if you can't find dry)
Dark rum

Chardonnay white wine (or dry white wine of choice)
Dry Vermouth

Berry liqueur, hazelnut and amaretto
Cognac
Dry red wine

FREQUENTLY USED PRODUCE STAPLES

Garlic
Shallots

Tomatoes
Onions

Potatoes (out of the light)

REFRIGERATOR STAPLES

Skim milk
Part skim milk Parmesan cheese
Miso (once opened, keep it in a zip-locked bag)
Lemons
Fat Free Mayonnaise
Non-Fat Plain Yogurt
Sesame oil
Olive oil (we recommened virgin)

Jar of minced garlic for quickie recipes
Parsley (fresh)
Prepared Dijon-style mustard
Almond paste (sometimes called Marzipan)
Fresh eggs
Oil-cured sun-dried tomatoes

Black bean sauce with chili
Sesame paste (Tahini)
Commerical salad dressings (we like Newman's Own)
Fruit speads and jellies for glazing and sweetening desserts
Fresh herbs–coriander, dill, basil, horseradish

FREEZER STAPLES

Concentrated fruit juices (we like Welch's berry juices), orange juice
Gingerroot (in zip-lock bag you can grate it straight from the freezer)

Nuts–pecans, almonds, hazelnuts, walnuts, sunflower seeds, pine nuts
Chicken stock (concentrated)

Herbs–dill, tarragon, basil, rosemary
Raspberries, blueberries, blackberries
Margarine

EQUIPMENT

Food processor
Blender
Yogurt funnel or cheesecloth
Nutmeg grater
Regular grater

Citrus grater
Chef's knife, paring knife
Dishwasher-safe cutting board x 2
Removeable bottom tart pan-12-inch

Mortar and pestle
Springform cake pan 7 inch & 10-inch
Large stockpot (for making stock & cooking pasta)

HERBS AND SPICES

A Brief Guide To Their Characteristics, Storage And Use

Herbs and Spices add that little extra touch to a dish. We use them. . .

* To complement a robust flavor
* To bring out a delicate flavor
* To accent sweet flavors
* To accent savory flavors
* To harmonize and add texture in judicious combinations

Herbs generally come from the leaf of the plant—**Spices** generally come from the seeds of the plant.

- *Herbs and spices are supposed to complement the food not dominate it.*
- *Herbs and spices should be bought in small quantities.*
- *Herbs and spices should be stored in airtight containers in a cool dark place.*
- *Herbs should generally be added nearer the end of the cooking time.*
- *Spices are generally added nearer the beginning of the cooking time.*

Although we make considerable use of herbs and spices in this book, we have taken care to use them in small amounts, and in limited combinations. It is exciting to discover the different flavors that the addition of herbs and spices contribute to food, but it can be disappointing if overdone in your enthusiasm. We hope the following information will guide you to experimenting on your own.

HERBS . . . are divided into three major categories.

Dominant Herbs stand alone and do not blend well together. They are usually best fresh, when available; otherwise, frozen or freeze-dried.

- *Dominant herbs can be interchangeable, but not universally. It is difficult to provide a list due to changing quantities, and the intricate flavor of the dishes in which they may be used. Look for our suggestions with individual recipes.*

Earthy Herbs usually retain good flavor when dry, and although distinctive, do not assert their flavors individually when blended together.

- *All earthy herbs are interchangeable, and they combine well with themselves, but should be used sparingly with character herbs.*

Accent Herbs do just what their name implies, they complement the flavor of others.

- *All accent herbs are interchangeable. They combine with any character and or earthy herbs, and with themselves.*

DOMINANT HERBS

Dominant herbs stand alone, and, therefore, do not blend well together. They combine well with accent herbs.

Basil —This is an herb that is far superior when fresh (frozen is second best), dried is boring. It is increasingly more readily available in supermarkets in neat little hydroponic packages. It is magnificent with pasta, seafood, in salads and shredded straight out of the garden in a sandwich with ripe tomatoes and sprouts. This herb can be used in larger quantities than most others. Basil is an annual and grows well in a sunny location in well drained soil. If you grow your own, pick the blossoms off to encourage leaf growth.

Dillweed — Use this herb sparingly as it can overwhelm. We love it with seafood and in spreads and dips. Also delicious in iced cucumber soup. Can be grown in the garden with very little effort, its fine feathery leaves, long stems and flat spread of tiny blossoms make a handsome feature in a vase with daisies and cosmos.

Coriander Leaf — This herb is also known as Chinese parsley and cilantro. It has a distinctive flavor which you either love or hate! Used widely in Mexican, Chinese and Indian cuisines. As with basil, it loses its distinctive flavor when dried. This herb is so readily available in supermarkets, it's hardly worth the garden space to grow your own.

Mint — Comes in a variety of flavors such as spearmint, peppermint, pineapple and orange mint to name a few. It will grow like a weed if you let it loose in your garden. As with the other dominant herbs, it is far superior if you can get it fresh. Try adding mint to your lemonade. Use it as a garnish for desserts and beverages. Also great with peas, either in soup or just a sprig added when cooking. It can have a fairly harsh flavor when used in excess, added in small amounts it can give a delightful cool lift to marinades and spreads.

Rosemary — This herb was made for lamb; reserve some to rub into the flesh near the end of the cooking time to be sure to capture the delicate pine-like flavor. It is also best used fresh. When dried the leaves become sharp like needles, thus should be steeped in hot water prior to use if substituting dried. It cultivates very easily in a container if you have some space in your kitchen near a sunny window. It thrives on neglect and an occasional drink of veggie water (that's water that you've cooked the broccoli or beans or other green vegetables in, without salt.

French Tarragon — Retains excellent flavor when frozen, and is acceptable when dried. Like coriander and mint, its distinct flavor can dominate. It is best in cooked dishes; add it near the end of cooking. It is particularly good with chicken and in tomato soup. To make tarragon vinegar (much prized in French cuisine for use in salads), blanch a generous sprig of fresh tarragon in some rapidly boiling water, then add it to the bottle of vinegar. You can leave it in the bottle, as the vinegar will preserve it.

Freezing Herbs:	By far the best method. Strip the leaves and flowers off the coarse stems and pack them into zip-lock bags, releasing the air before sealing. Break off portions as needed and chop while still frozen. Chives, chervil, tarragon, basil, dill and lemon thyme freeze well. Be sure to label them because they will look very much alike when frozen.

EARTHY HERBS

Earthy herbs are also character herbs, but they differ from character herbs in that they combine with each other. They are mostly used in soups and stews where a robust flavor is desired. Most earthy herbs are an ingredient of bouquet garni which is a French seasoning used in stocks, soups and stews. Most earthy herbs dry well for storage.

Bay Leaf — Buy the whole leaf. Used in bouquet garni. It enhances braised and stewed dishes. It is usually removed before serving.

Marjoram — A close relative of oregano with a more subtle flavor. We prefer it to the latter, for it retains good flavor when dried, and combines well with all other earthy herbs and most character herbs. Marjoram is used widely in Italian and Spanish dishes, such as in pizza sauces and savory rice.

Thyme — We love lemon thyme which is not as available as regular, but grows abundantly in northern climates and is available dry in specialty stores. Although it is more lemony when fresh, it does not lose much in the drying process. It combines well with other earthy herbs and all accent herbs. Great in stews and braised dishes, it is also delicious in salads and spreads. It is one of the ingredients for bouquet garni.

ACCENT HERBS

These are the universal "go-withs." They are always added towards the end of the cooking time, or more often as a garnish just before serving. They combine well with dominant and earthy herbs and with themselves.

Chives — Related to onions and garlic, but with a milder flavor. They are best used fresh, and are great in salads and sprinkled on most vegetables. Fresh chives folded into drained yogurt is a great accompaniment to baked potatoes. You can buy them fresh in many supermarkets year round; however, if you have some space in your garden, they come up year after year and have a pretty lilac blossom which is excellent as a garnish.

Garlic — Readily available fresh and worth the extra effort. Garlic adds excitement to most savory dishes and salads and reduces the need for salt. Select large, firm unblemished heads; remove any visible green shoots, as they can be bitter and indigestible. Take care when cooking with garlic not to burn it. It's very satisfying, requires very little effort to grow, and is so sweet and fresh.

Nasturtium — We like to shred their tender leaves to add a spicy touch to salads and sandwiches. The blossoms make a bold and beautiful statement as a garnish on a crudité platter, floating on cold soups, or in salads, and they're also good to eat. Nasturtiums are an annual, and grow prolifically in a sunny location in the garden or in pots and bloom all summer long.

Parsley — There are two varieties available, Curly and Italian. Curly is more attractive as a garnish, whereas Italian has a more distinctive flavor. If you can't find one, use the other. Parsley has a fairly delicate flavor. Since it is so readily available, we recommend you use it fresh. Add it just before serving.

SPICES

Spices offer more opportunities for substitutions, but these are so wide and varied we are still not going to supply you with the list.

Cayenne Pepper — A combination of hot red pepper and spices, which is used in many hot sauces. Great to pep up a bland dish, and helps reduce the need for salt.

Celery Seeds — A versatile spice which is used in soups, salads and sauces. It combines well with most other spices.

Cinnamon — A sweet spice, it retains good flavor when ground. It is used in a variety of desserts, beverages and savory dishes. Cinnamon sticks along with nutmeg, cloves and orange peel give a pleasant festive flavor to hot apple cider and or mulled red wine.

Cloves — Have a very assertive flavor, so use them sparingly. Use whole to flavor beverages or ground in spice cakes and breads. Cloves combine well when used sparingly with cinnamon, nutmeg and ginger.

Coriander Seeds — This spice is the seed of leaf coriander with a distinctive flavor and is a highly versatile spice. It combines well with cumin, cinnamon, celery seeds and mustard seeds. It is one of the spices used to make curry flavors.

Cumin — A versatile spice which is used widely in Indian and Mexican cuisines, an ingredient of curry powder and chili seasoning.

Ginger — A delightfully fragrant spice which is indispensable in Chinese cuisine. It adds an exotic touch to soups, seafood and salads, and is also great in marinades. Buy smooth-skinned roots in small amounts and keep it in your freezer. You can grate it while still frozen.

Mustard Seeds — Come black and white, with black having a stronger flavor. A combination of black and white mustard seeds are the primary ingredient in most prepared mustards. Mustards aid in calorie reduction when used instead of mayonnaise in sandwiches. They are also widely used as a condiment on meats and seafoods, thus helping reduce the need for salt.

Nutmeg — Is a fragrant and exotic spice, which is best when freshly grated. It adds an exotic and somewhat nutty touch to vegetables, beverages, and sauces both sweet and savory.

Paprika — is the concentrated powder of sweet red pepper. Hungarian paprika has the best flavor. Try sprinkling it on grilled meats and seafood. It is also aesthetically pleasing as it helps meats brown more quickly.

Poppy Seed — These tiny black seeds add a special nutty flavor when sprinkled on breads. They are also great to add a delicate crunch on cakes and cookies.

Saffron — An exotic spice which is the stamen of the autumn crocus. It has a most unusual flavor and is prized in Indian, Morrocan and Spanish cuisines. Beware of cheap imitations— the real thing does not turn black when heated—and always buy the whole threads. Light roasting makes it more brittle, thus is helpful in grinding.

Sesame Seeds — A light roasting brings out the flavor of these nutty little seeds. Great for an added crunch to sweet and savory dishes. Particularly good on breads. Used as the primary ingredients of Gomasio, which extends the flavor of salt.

SAVORY COMBINATIONS OF DRIED HERBS AND SPICES

TO SHAKE ON PREPARED FOOD AND ADD TO MARINADES

SPICY LEMON SEASONING:

Try using 1/2 teaspoon of this seasoning rubbed into a chicken breast. Wrap the breast in lightly oiled cheesecloth, and bake at 375°F for 45 minutes to 1 hour (depending on the size of the breast).

2 tablespoons lemon zest
2 teaspoons dried marjoram
2 teaspoons lemon thyme (use regular if unavailable)
1/8 teaspoon bay leaf, crumbled
1/4 teaspoon black peppercorns, freshly ground
14 dehydrated garlic flakes, ground with mortar and pestle

1/2 teaspoon dehydrated onion flakes
1 tablespoon freeze-dried chives (ground with mortar and pestle)
1/2 teaspoon celery seeds, lightly roasted and ground
1/4 teaspoon green peppercorns, ground
1/8 teaspoon lemon oil (if available)

☐ Toss all together and store in a shaker container or screw top jar with holes in the lid.

SPICY HOT SEASONING WITH SESAME SEEDS:

1/4 cup sesame seeds, lightly roasted and ground a little
1/4 teaspoon black pepper, freshly ground
1 teaspoon dried sweet red pepper flakes (or 1/2 teaspoon Hungarian paprika)
1/2 teaspoon coriander seeds, lightly roasted and coarsely ground
1/2 teaspoon whole cumin seeds, lightly roasted and coarsely ground

1/4 teaspoon cayenne pepper
1/2 teaspoon whole celery seeds, lightly roasted and ground
1/2 teaspoon orange zest
1/8 teaspoon orange oil (if available)
1/2 teaspoon onion flakes, ground a little
1/4 teaspoon garlic flakes, ground a little
1 teaspoon sun dried tomato, chopped finely

☐ Toss all together and store in shaker jar or screw top jar with holes in the lid.
☐ NOTE: Experiment with your own substitutions if you are unable to find some of the above ingredients.

SALAD PREPARATION

and some Good Greens to know

Lettuce must be fresh. To help retain freshness observe the following:
a) Keep the outer leaves on until ready to use.
b) When washing, use plenty of cold running water, but wash quickly, and dry immediately (salad spinners are great for this). If your lettuce is home grown without pesticides and is not gritty there is no reason to wash it.
c) Store in a sealed container in your refrigerator.

Vinegar can overwhelm, keep it to a minimum, and use a good wine or fruit vinegar not too high in acid content. Appealing alternatives to vinegar are citrus juices such as lemon, lime and orange. You might experiment with fresh pineapple juice and apple cider.

Toss your salad just before serving so as not to wilt the lettuce, unless of course it is a marinated vegetable salad, or a wilted salad.

Combine your salads with thought to the blending of flavors and textures. While contrast can be exciting, too much variation could lose a subtle flavor. The following list should act as a guide to your blending of many interesting and well balanced salads.

Some Good Greens to Know

Endive though strictly a vegetable, adds a delicious crunch with a slight suggestion of bitterness. It is pale yellow, conical in shape and has tightly interwoven leaves. Available in winter to early spring. Shred into a matchstick julienne and add to a first course salad.

Bibb lettuce could be described as piquant. It is a crisper version of Boston lettuce, is smaller and has more compact leaves. Watercress and endive marry very well with Bibb lettuce. Try this combination with a walnut oil and lime viniagrette.

Boston lettuce has a delicate melt in the mouth flavor, somewhat buttery. Take care not to overwhelm the delicate flavor of this lettuce with too many other additions. Try it with some borage blossoms and freshly snipped chives using a light lemon vinaigrette and the addition of fresh lemon thyme if available.

Curley Endive Otherwise known as Chicory and or Endive lettuce (not be be confused with Belgian Endive). This is your sociable lettuce, it stands up very well when combined with other greens. It has a distinctive mustardy flavor, and is complimented by a hearty viniagrette using Sherry Wine Vinegar and a fruity olive oil. This lettuce has a sturdy shelf life and holds up very well as a garnish.

Iceberg lettuce has its place for its crispness, generally in Mexican dishes, but personally it does not rate highly on our list, mostly for its lack of nutrient content.

Leaf lettuce is attractive with its frilly edges, it has a delicate flavor, and can easily be overwhelmed in a crowded salad bowl. Use it up quickly as it is highly perishable.

Romaine lettuce is an excellent addition to a mixed green salad, it has a distinctive slightly bitter flavor and retains its crispness. Use only the inner pale yellow leaves, the outer leaves tend to be tough. In choosing this lettuce at the supermarket, go for the more compact ones. Avoid dark spots on the leaves.

Sorrel is an excellent spring or summer vegetable. Try it in tossed salads for its tangy bite. Will add piquancy to sauces when cooked, particularly good with fish. Choose small pale green leaves no longer then 6 to 8 inches. Very easy to grow, and will come up year after year, if you have space in your garden.

Spinach a good meaty leaf with lots of flavor. Best in spring and early summer. Take care in choosing your spinach to avoid gritty leaves as the grit can become embedded into the leaves and will not wash off. If you can find the loose leaf bundles they are usually fresher and have more flavor than the packaged variety. Choose dark shiny leaves. Wash thoroughly in several batches of cold water before use, spin dry as their irregular shaped leaves retain a lot of moisture.

Watercress is really an herb, and lends a superb mustardy flavor to iced summer soups, yogurt cheese, and combines well in a tossed green salad. Choose dark green plump leaves with firm stems. Store submerged in water in your refrigerator, being sure to change the water daily. Also attractive as a garnish and in sandwiches.

GLOSSARY

Acceptable Margarine: Margarines that have liquid oil as their first ingredient followed by hydrogenated oil. Saturated fat should be less than 2 grams per 1 tablespoon serving.

Al dente: Usually used to describe cooked pasta, with a bite, not overdone, tender but firm

Blanch: We use this method for vegetables. Immerse in boiling water in preparation for a veggie salad or prior to freezing. It brings out the color, and makes the veggies more absorbent before adding dressing

Blend: To thoroughly combine ingredients

Boil: To heat liquid until bubbly

Broil: To cook by direct exposure to intense heat such as a flame or an electric heating unit

Bruise: To soften or partially crush

Clove of Garlic: One section of the whole bulb

Dice: To cut into small cubes

Dredge: To cover with flour or some kind of coating

Dust: A light coating of flour, confectioners' sugar, etc.

Julienne: To cut into thin strips about the size of matches

Lemon or Orange Zest: The outer peel of a lemon, orange or other citrus fruit

Marinate: To soak in a liquid, usually with herbs and spices to tenderize and add flavor

Marzipan: Almond paste or a confection made with almond paste

Mince: To chop finely

Miso: A fermented soy product used to enhance the flavor of foods where sodium is decreased, available in health food stores.

Orange Segment: One section of the whole orange

Paté: A paste, usually savory, for spreading on crackers or bread. Sometimes used to stuff meats and fish

Poach: To cook in simmering liquid

Purée: To render very smooth, either pressing through a sieve or spinning in a food processor or blender

Sauté: To cook in a skillet on top of the stove with a little oil or lubricant

Score: To make shallow cuts with a knife or razor blade

Shred: To finely slice diagonally, pull apart or grate into small pieces

Simmer: To cook just below boiling point on top of the stove

Steamer Basket: A piece of equipment that fits into a saucepan to convert it into a steamer

Steam: To cook over boiling water, or in a tightly sealed pot with very little water

Yogurt Cheese Products: Such as yogurt cheese and yogurt sour cream (see page 34)

Zester: A small utensil used to remove the outer peel from citrus fruit

HIGH FIT - LOW FAT SUBSTITUTIONS
If you don't have one use the other!

shallot	scallions
Vidalia or walla walla onions	scallions or shallots
apple cider	apple juice, or reconstituted frozen concentrate
fresh orange juice	reconstituted frozen orange juice
hazelnuts	almonds
oat bran	oatmeal (ground in the food processor)
olive oil	canola oil
fresh artichoke hearts	frozen artichoke hearts, no added salt
tamari sauce	low sodium soy sauce
butternut squash	acorn squash
wild rice	brown rice, or some of the Lunhdberg combinations of rices
raspberry vinegar	white wine vinegar (add crushed strained frozen raspberries if available)
Sherry wine vinegar	2/3 red wine vinegar plus 1/3 dry Sherry
blackberries	blueberries
apples	pears

RECIPE MODIFICATIONS FOR LOWERING TOTAL FAT, SATURATED FAT, AND CHOLESTEROL

FOR	TRY
1 whole egg	2 egg whites
1 cup butter	1 cup margarine
1 cup shortening or lard	3/4 cup vegetable oil
1/2 cup shortening	1/3 cup vegetable oil
1 cup whole milk	1 cup skim milk
1 cup light cream	1 cup evaporated skim milk
1 cup sour cream	1 cup plain nonfat yogurt or 1 cup low-fat cottage cheese, blended with 2 tablespoons lemon juice until creamy
1 ounce regular cheese	1 ounce skim milk cheese or part-skim milk cheese, with 6 grams of fat or less per ounce
1 tablespoon salad dressing	1 tablespoon low-calorie salad dressing
1 ounce (1 square) baking chocolate	3 tablespoons powdered cocoa plus 1 tablespoon oil

INDEX

RECIPE INDEX

Notes

1. This table is reprinted from Committees of the American Diabetes Association, Inc, and The American Dietetic Association, 1977. *A guide for professionals: The effective application of exchange lists for meal planning*, p. 17. (page 16)

2. Based on information provided in J.P. Grant, P.B. Custer, and J. Thurlow. Current techniques of nutritional assessment. *Surg. Clin. North Am.* 61:437, 1981. (page 16)

3. Based on information provided in Gail L. Becker, R.D., *Heart Smart–a plan for low-cholesterol living*, page 44, Merrell Dow, Second Edition. (page 16)

ORDER FORM

High Fit – Low Fat

Mail to: MedSport, University of Michigan Medical Center
P.O. Box 363, Ann Arbor, MI 48106-0363

Please send _____ copy(s) of **High Fit – Low Fat**
_____ @ $14.95 each
_____ + $2.40 shipping and handling (for first book)
_____ + $1.50 shipping and handling (each additional book
        to the same address)
_____ Michigan residents: add 4% sales tax
_____ Total

Name _____

Address _____

City/State/Zip _____

Daytime Phone _____

My payment is by:
☐ Check   ☐ Money Order   ☐ Visa   ☐ MasterCard

Credit Card Number (all digits)_____

Expiration Date_____

Signature _____
(required if using credit card)

Make checks payable to: University of Michigan